THE diabetic COOKBOOK

SARAH BANBERY

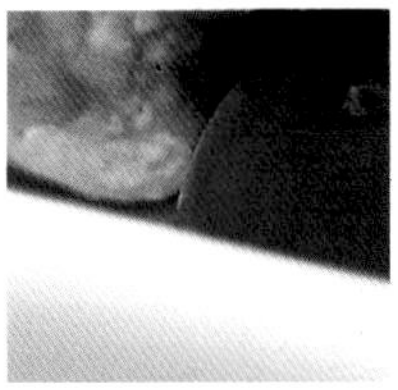 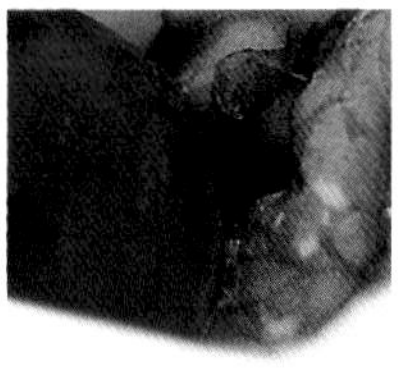 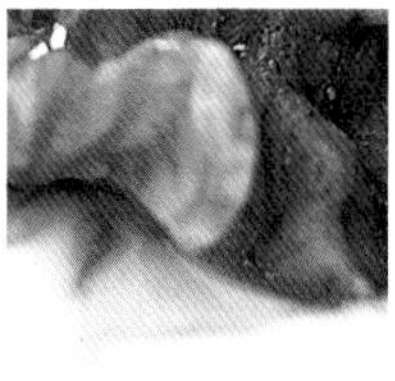  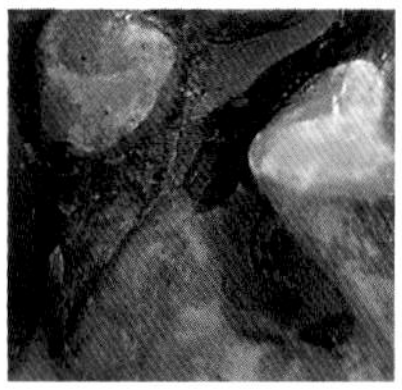 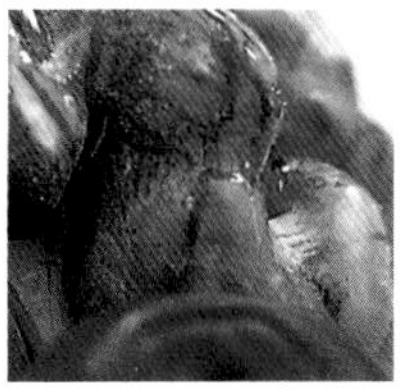

This is a Parragon Book
First published in 2004

Parragon
Queen Street House
4 Queen Street
Bath
BA1 1HE
UK

Designed and produced by
THE BRIDGEWATER BOOK COMPANY

Nutritional facts and analysis: *Charlotte Watts*
Photography: *Clive Bozzard-Hill*
Home Economist: *Philippa Vanstone*
Stylist: *Angela Macfarlane*

The publishers would like to thank the following companies for the loan of props: *Dartington Crystal, Marlux Mills, Maxwell & Williams, Lifestyle Collections, Viners & Oneida, Typoon and John Lewis.*

Printed in China

ISBN: 1-40544-582-3

NOTES FOR THE READER

This book uses metric and imperial measurements. Follow the same units of measurement throughout; do not mix metric and imperial. All spoon measements are level, unless otherwise stated: teaspoons are assumed to be 5 ml and tablespoons are assumed to be 15 ml.

Individual vegetables such as potatoes are medium and pepper is freshly ground black pepper. Milk used in the recipes is skimmed or semi-skimmed to help limit the fat content of the meal. The recipes have been made with a reduced-fat and -sugar content in accordance with healthy eating guidelines. However, this means that they will not keep fresh for as long a period of time as their higher-fat and -sugar alternatives.

Some of the recipes require stock. If you use commercially made stock granules or cubes, these can have a relatively high salt content, so do not add any further salt. If you make your own stock, keep the fat and salt content to a minimum. Don't fry the vegetables before simmering – just simmer the vegetables, herbs and meat, poultry or fish in water and strain. Meat and poultry stocks should be strained, cooled and refrigerated before use so that the fat from the meat rises to the top and solidifies – it can then be easily removed and this reduces the saturated fat content of the meal. Homemade stocks should be stored in the refrigerator and used within two days, or frozen in usable portions and labelled.

Recipes using raw or very lightly cooked eggs should be avoided by infants, the elderly, pregnant women, convalescents and anyone suffering from an illness.

Ovens should be preheated to the specified temperature. If using a fan-assisted oven, check the manufacturer's instructions for adjusting the time and temperature.

The values of the nutritional analysis for each recipe refer to a single serving, or a single slice where relevant. They do not include the serving suggestion. Where a range of portions is given the nutritional analysis figure refers to the mid-range figure. The calorific value given is in KCal (Kilocalories). The carbohydrate figure includes starches and sugars, with the sugar value then given separately. The fat figure is likewise the total fat, with the saturated part then given separately.

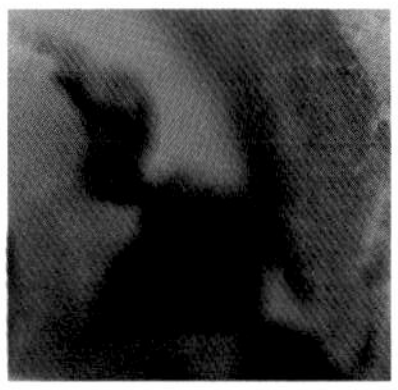 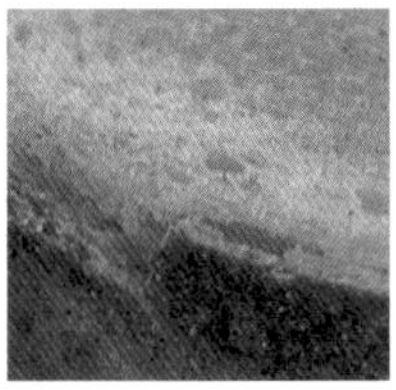 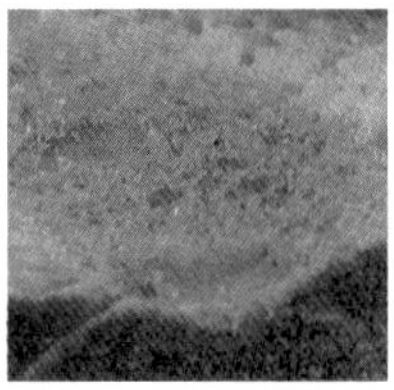 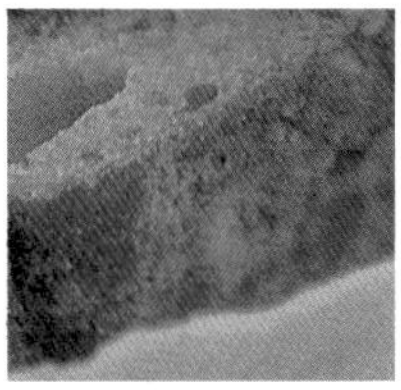 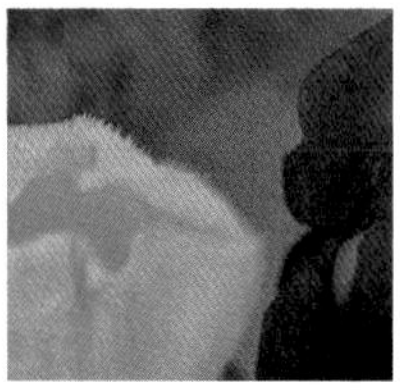 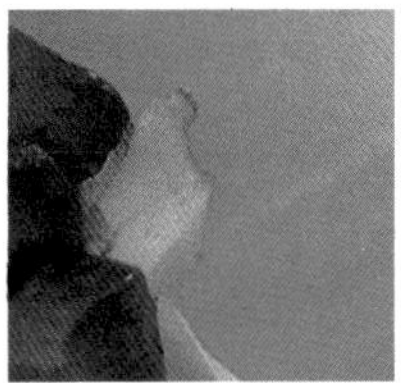

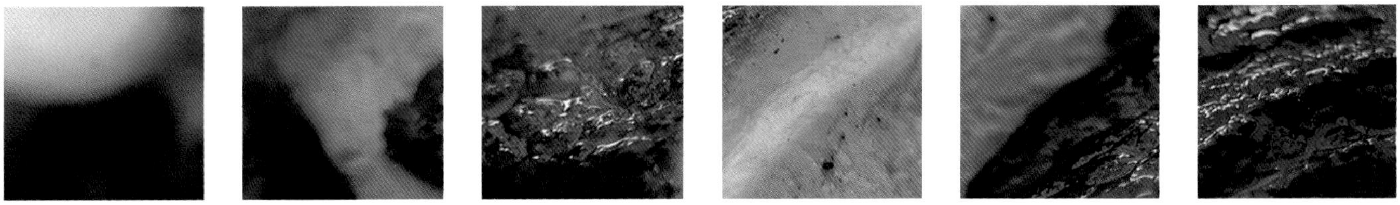

contents

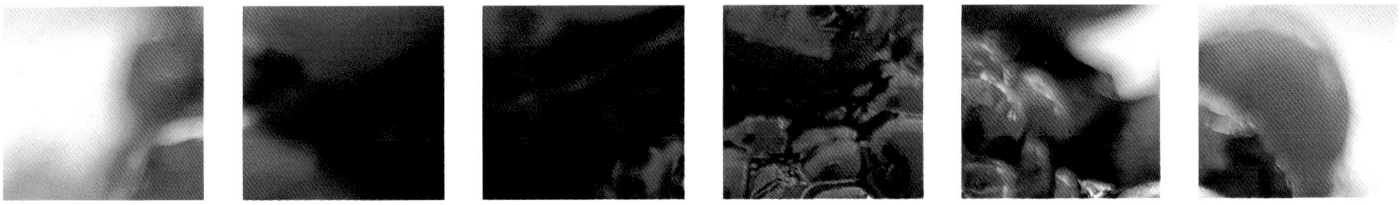

Introduction

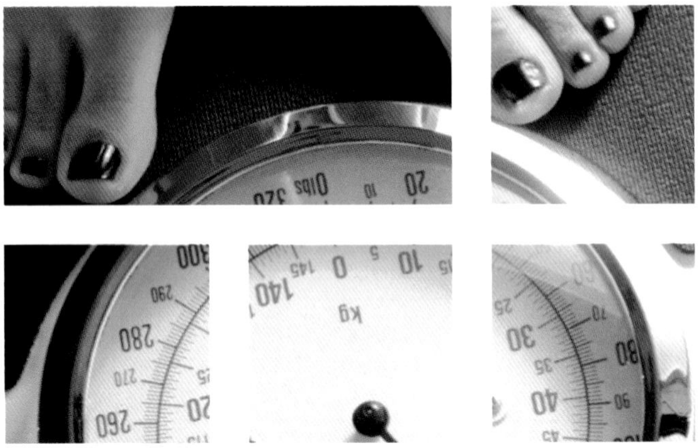

The diet that is most beneficial for a person with diabetes is actually healthy for anyone, especially if you want to reduce your risk of developing common conditions such as heart disease and stroke, high cholesterol, high blood pressure and, of course, diabetes, if you have a family history of it. This book provides simple, sensible eating guidelines and recipes that will benefit all those with diabetes and the whole family besides, and offers a good starting point for establishing dietary awareness and taking control of your health. These dietary guidelines can also help you to manage your weight, in conjunction with a suitable exercise programme and a controlled daily calorie intake. The recipes are also delicious, and the enjoyment of food is, after all, a very important factor. But this pleasure can be doubled if you know that what you are putting in your mouth is of benefit to your well-being and could significantly improve your quality of life.

The Nature of Diabetes

Diabetes is a condition characterized by an inability to produce the hormone insulin from the pancreas and therefore move glucose from the bloodstream into the cells and muscles where it is needed to produce energy. This causes an excess of sugar or glucose in the blood, which can lead to conditions associated with diabetes, such as obesity, heart disease, high cholesterol and damage to nerves (neuropathies), eyes (retinopathy) and kidneys.

There are two types of diabetes:

Type I Diabetes is also called Insulin-Dependent Diabetes Mellitus (IDDM) and develops when the body stops producing insulin. This is due to the destruction of the cells in the pancreas that make insulin and it is believed to be a genetic condition. In most people it manifests before the age of 40 and must be controlled by injections and diet.

Type II Diabetes is also called Non-Insulin-Dependent Diabetes Mellitus (NIDDM), or adult-onset diabetes. This can occur as a result of a diet high in refined foods or sugars, where the pancreas has to produce so much insulin that it finally becomes exhausted and either produces less insulin or is unable to use the insulin that it does produce, leading to symptoms. This condition is also related to weight gain and a diet that helps control blood sugar is also effective for weight loss.

The same diet is advocated for both types of diabetes, but anyone would benefit from this dietary approach and the recipes in this book, as the main goals are to lose weight, protect the heart and lower cholesterol to decrease the risk of associated conditions. For Type II, in some cases, if the diet is properly controlled and under medical supervision, this can help to reduce the amount of medication that needs to be taken.

Some people also suffer from a condition called **Syndrome X**, a potentially pre-diabetic state where the body becomes insensitive to insulin, and therefore cannot use it properly, leading to weight gain. Symptoms of untreated diabetes include increased thirst, frequent urination with large volumes, fatigue, weight loss, skin and genital itching. If you have a combination of these and previous high sugar intake, see your doctor to check for diabetes. If you don't, these dietary guidelines could still help to relieve your symptoms, and if there is diabetes in your family, this diet can help to decrease your risk of developing it.

The Role of Nutrition in the Management of Diabetes

In relation to diabetes, 'management' means to maintain near normal blood-sugar levels and increase the effectiveness of insulin in the body so that less is needed. This is called 'increasing insulin sensitivity'. As mentioned with Syndrome X (see box, left), people can be 'insulin insensitive' and still produce insulin, so the following dietary advice will also be very helpful for them.

Insulin is normally released when sugar levels in the blood become higher than they should be. People with diabetes cannot reduce these blood-sugar levels without the aid of administered insulin. It was previously thought that this problem could be avoided by excluding carbohydrates entirely from the diet, but this has now been refuted. Carbohydrates are our main source of energy and should make up half our daily calorie intake. It is the kind of carbohydrates we eat and when that is crucial.

If you have Type I diabetes, the amount and timing of consumption of carbohydrates should be balanced with your dosage and timing of insulin medication. This needs to be discussed with your doctor.

If you have Type II diabetes, the relative lack of production of insulin should be considered and carbohydrate intake spread throughout the day. Again, this should be discussed with your doctor, especially if you are taking any medication.

The aim of the diet in this book is to keep blood-glucose levels as close to normal as possible, and this can be very simple and easy to achieve. A few basic changes to your diet that can make you feel better are very motivating. With blood-sugar control, when you eat is all-important; eating little and often maintains a slow, steady stream of glucose to the blood and a good breakfast sets the right levels for the day, meaning fewer cravings and more control over the food choices you make.

If blood-sugar levels are not properly controlled, damage can occur in the eyes, kidneys, heart, legs and brain. This is also why exercise is crucial; it helps blood-sugar control and increases circulation to these body parts, which helps to limit damage. Diet has also been shown to improve insulin sensitivity. This means that for those who produce some insulin, it can become more effective, and for those who produce none and need to medicate, they may find their levels easier to control. This also helps to limit the potential damage to arteries that high insulin levels have been shown to increase.

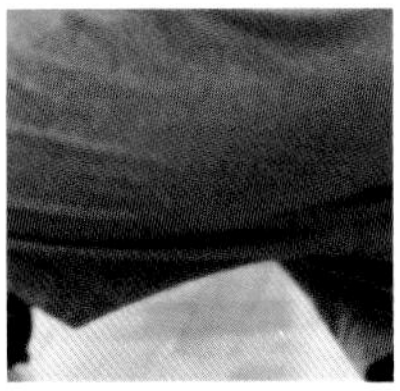
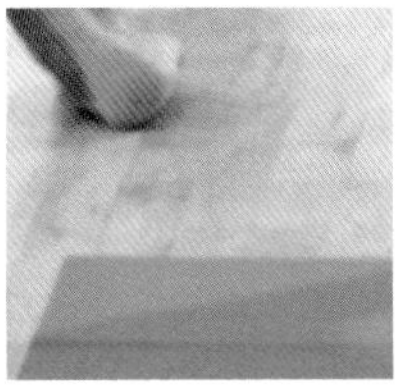

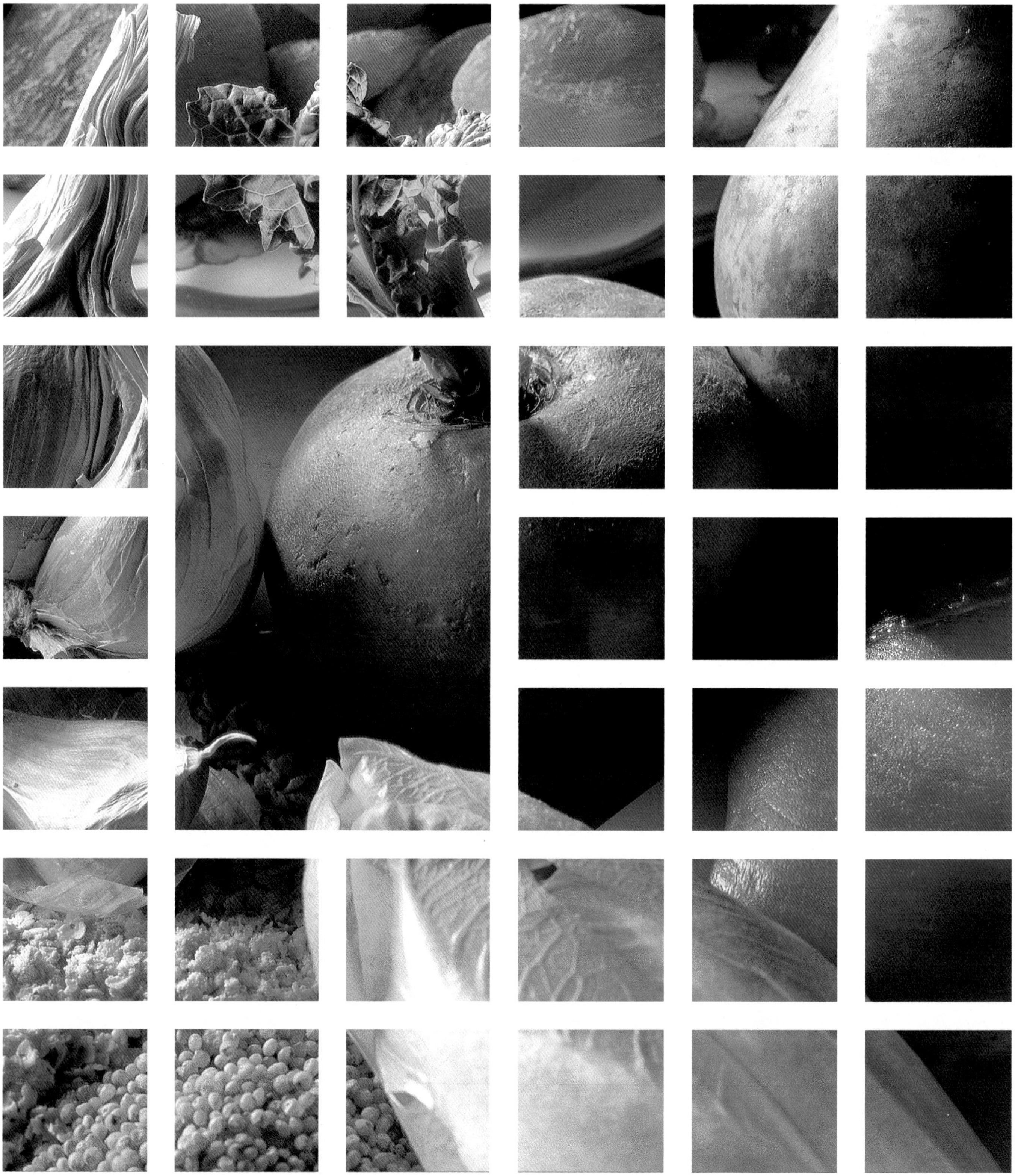

The Dietary Approach to Diabetes Management

As diabetes is heightened when blood-sugar levels become raised, the advice is to balance these levels by avoiding highs and lows. Sugar, salt, caffeine, alcohol, cigarettes and refined and processed foods such as white bread, cake and pastries cause a rush of sugar into the bloodstream and should be avoided. After this initial surge, blood-sugar levels can then drop dramatically, even causing hypoglycaemia, with symptoms such as sweating, hunger, anxiety, irritability, rapid heart rate, palpitations, blurred vision, tingling lips and turning pale. Hypoglycaemia can also be caused by too much medication (consult your doctor) or alcohol, which inhibits glucose production by the liver. To avoid these sudden dips in blood-sugar levels, try to keep them even by not missing meals and following the dietary advice given here. This can help stop imbalances that lead to vicious cycles, as foods that raise blood-sugar levels can create cravings for more of the same.

Many other conditions such as depression, headaches, fatigue and insomnia are affected by fluctuating blood-sugar levels, and as they lead to high cholesterol and heart disease risk, this dietary advice is appropriate for everyone.

With diabetes, the balance of macronutrients – carbohydrates, fats and proteins – is crucial. Diabetes UK, the HEA (Health Education Authority) and WHO (World Health Organization) all recommend a diet high in complex carbohydrates, low in saturated fat and high in fibre. This is because it is the combination of saturated fat and sugar that causes the accumulation of fat which increases insulin insensitivity, diabetes symptoms, risks and side effects.

Carbohydrates

Carbohydrates, found in vegetables, fruit, grains and dairy products, are made from simple sugars, which all eventually break down to glucose. While carbohydrates are our main source of fuel and should make up half of our daily calorie intake, it is vital to make the right choice of the type of carbohydrate to be eaten, depending on the speed in which it breaks down into the glucose components in the body.

Refined carbohydrates or sugars are very simple molecules. What we call 'sugar' for cooking and eating is actually sucrose – just two molecules of glucose that offer a very quick supply of sugar to the bloodstream, demanding a high need for insulin that the diabetic cannot supply. Sucrose is found in processed foods, sweets, cakes, soft drinks, fruit juices and very refined carbohydrates such as white bread, where the bran part of the wheat has been stripped away. This quick release of sugar can be laid down as fat if the body cannot employ insulin to use it correctly. Current research has shown that many diabetics may be eating more sugar than they think, because many have a reduced ability to taste sugar. Bringing down high blood-sugar levels is a priority; converting sugars into fat takes place in the liver and can lead to the obesity that is often associated with diabetes.

Complex carbohydrates, known as starches, release their sugars more slowly, so are used for energy rather than laid down as fat. These are termed starches. They also contain fibre, which also helps to slow down sugar release and eliminate toxins from the body to help prevent disease. The wholegrain bran part of cereal grains that is removed in white flour and processed foods contains fibre and provides glucose molecules that are bound together in more complex structures. Vegetables and fruit in their natural, raw state provide complex carbohydrates bound in fibre. They therefore take much more time to break down into their simple sugars and provide a more slow and steady release into the bloodstream, which is much easier for someone with little insulin to deal with. Pasta, potatoes, brown rice and brown bread can be eaten in a diabetic diet if the appropriate fat-intake guidelines are also observed and they are eaten with proteins to slow down their release of sugars.

The carbohydrate issue is, however, not as simple as previously thought – see the Glycaemic Index (pages 10–11).

Fibre

Fibre can either be soluble or insoluble and a balance of both in the diet is very important for health in those with diabetes. Fibre helps to level out blood sugar by slowing down digestion and the release of sugar from food. Aim for 35 grams per day to balance blood sugar, lower cholesterol levels, clean the colon of toxins and to help prevent heart disease.

Soluble fibre tends to be found in fruit and vegetables, such as apples, citrus fruits, carrots, cherries, avocados, beetroot, dried apricots and prunes, and also some seed husks such as linseed, oat bran and psyllium husks, which many people take to counter constipation. It helps digestion by absorbing water and softening stools, and this can help lower cholesterol.

Insoluble fibre remains undigested and so clears the digestive system, prevents constipation, lessens the incidence of colon and rectal cancer and speeds up the elimination of waste from the body. It is found in brown rice (the fibre is removed when processed to white), rye bread and crackers, lentils, asparagus, Brussels sprouts, cabbage, other wholegrains and fibrous vegetables.

Oats are a complex carbohydrate, none of which turns directly into sugar in the body. They provide 10 per cent of their weight in fibre and are a perfect breakfast food. Vegetables and fruit contain cellulose, an insoluble plant fibre that contains little sugar, but it is important to remember that when cooked these become broken down more readily into sugars. This is why vegetables such as carrots, peppers and parsnips taste sweeter the longer they are cooked.

Fats

The stipulation of a high-carbohydrate, low-fat diet for diabetics does not mean that all fats should be avoided. Instead, it is a matter of choosing the right fats and consuming them in moderation. Lowering your intake of refined carbohydrates that cause the accumulation of body fat is a big factor, and including a controlled amount of beneficial oils and essential fats in your diet can lower cholesterol and help blood-sugar regulation.

Saturated fats tend to be from animal sources, such as butter and meat fats. They are solid at room temperature and can form in the same way in the body – if eaten in high amounts they can clog arteries and add to the risk of heart disease. In combination with sugars, they can become laid down as fat, and so foods combining both, such as pastries, are the main culprits of weight gain.

Monounsaturated oils are vegetable in origin and those traditionally eaten in Mediterranean countries, namely olive, almond, hazelnut, peanut and avocado oils. They contain a fatty acid called oleic acid or omega-9 and remain liquid at room temperature, but begin to solidify when refrigerated. These have been found to have a neutral effect on blood cholesterol, although an excess can raise fat levels in the blood. The exception is olive oil, which has been shown actually to reduce blood cholesterol. However, this effect is thought to be caused by unique active components rather than the monounsaturated fat content. These are less damaged by heat than oils that stay liquid when chilled and therefore can be used for cooking.

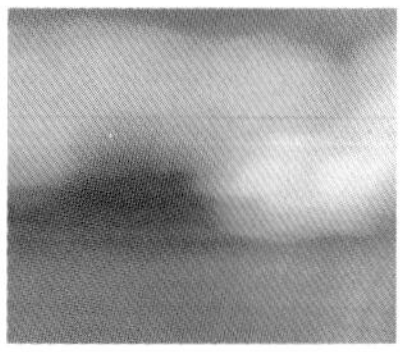

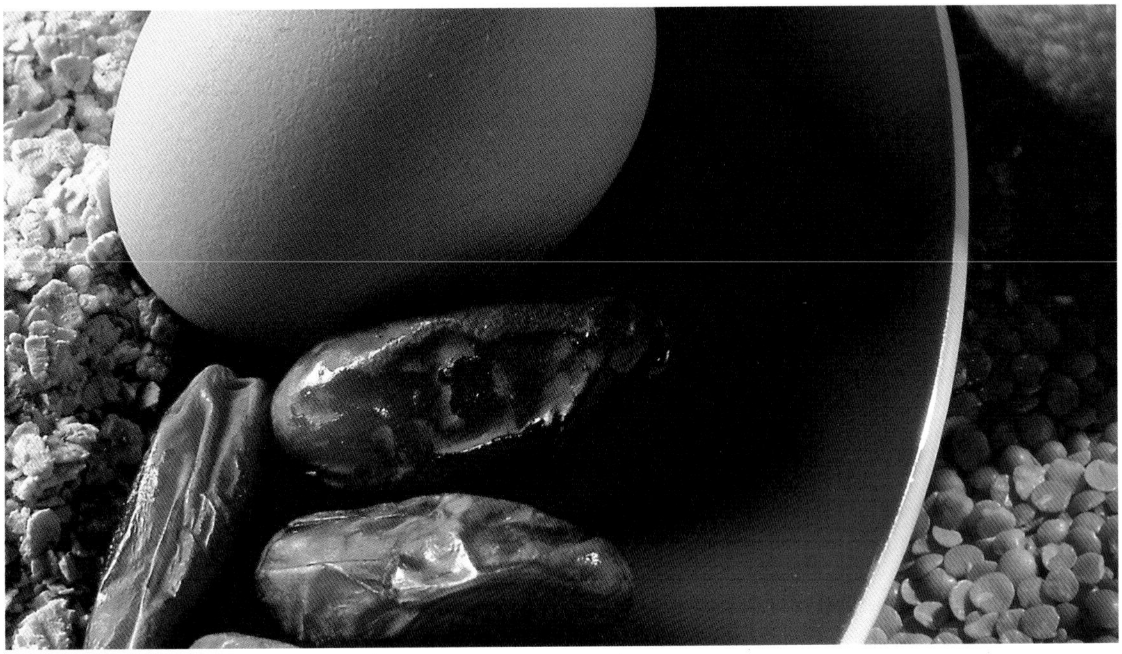

Polyunsaturated fatty acids are always liquid and contain the essential fatty acids, the omega-6 oils, that help to produce localized hormones in the body, which are important for blood-sugar regulation. These include sesame, soya, sunflower, walnut, pumpkin and hemp oils. They are termed 'essential' because they are crucial to body functions and must be consumed as they cannot be made in the body. Saturated fats can actually stop essential fats being used at a cellular level.

In the case of both polyunsaturated and monounsaturated fats, eating the nuts, seeds and vegetables from which these oils are produced can also play a vital role in the effective management of diabetes. For example, the American Diabetes Association classes avocados as a 'superfood' for diabetics, since not only do they contain beneficial oils but they also contain many nutrients that are important for cholesterol management and the protection of arteries against damage. Plant sterols (sterols are types of fat) help to reduce bad cholesterol and lutein helps to protect the eyes against diabetes-related degeneration. Although avocados, olives, nuts and seeds also contain some saturated fats and should be eaten in moderation, they provide omega-6 oils, vitamin E, vitamins B_3 and B_6, zinc and magnesium, which all aid blood-sugar management.

Omega-3 oils are those found in oily fish such as salmon, tuna, herring, mackerel, trout and sardines. Like the omega-6 oils, these are essential fatty acids and are crucial to our health. Much research has shown how important these are for heart health; they should be eaten 3–4 times a week, in variety. Both omega-3 and omega-6 oils protect parts of the body that are rich in fats, and these areas of the body may commonly become damaged in a person with diabetes – the eyes, kidneys, liver and circulation from the heart. For vegetarians, hemp, pumpkin, soya and walnut oils contain some omega-3 oils but are higher in omega-6. Omega-3 and omega-6 should be eaten in a one-to-one ratio and flax or linseed can be added to food as a source of omega-3 oils.

Proteins

Proteins are the major source of building materials for the body. They can also be used as a source of energy that is released very slowly. They are therefore very good for blood-sugar management and can slow down sugar release into the bloodstream if eaten with less complex carbohydrates. Caution should be taken not to obtain these mainly from high-fat sources such as meats, but also from eggs, low-fat dairy products and vegetable sources such as pulses and beans and in small amounts from other vegetables such as broccoli and cauliflower.

The Glycaemic Index (GI)

Research into sugars and their release into the bloodstream has found that some foods behave in a surprising way when introduced into the body. It is no longer enough just to distinguish between simple sugars and complex carbohydrates in the diabetic kitchen. As we are unable to predict how a food will act by its sugar and starch content alone, a table called the Glycaemic Index has been drawn up to compare the release of sugar into the bloodstream that foods create against a measure of 100 for glucose. In the table, foods are categorized into high, medium and low. High (more than 70) means that sugars are released very quickly, near to the speed of glucose itself. These foods should not be eaten on their own or they can cause a quick increase of blood sugar. They can, however, be eaten in small amounts at the same time as a food with a low score (under 55). This would equal a combined score in the medium range (55–70) and a good control of blood sugar. You should aim to include as many foods in the low range as possible for the best blood-sugar control and include those in the medium or high categories only with protein or other low-GI foods.

A low-GI diet can help to increase the body's sensitivity to insulin so that the insulin you do have works more effectively and less damage is likely to occur to nerves. It can also help to keep blood fats low, in conjunction with a low-saturated fat diet, and therefore reduce heart disease-related risks.

Certain foods shown in the table may surprise you in terms of release of sugars – corn flakes and parsnips, for instance, have very high scores and should be eaten with foods that bring the score down overall. Proteins and oils are not included in the Glycaemic Index as they are known to be low-GI foods since they do not contain carbohydrates. Therefore, they can be eaten with the high-GI foods to slow down sugar release, for instance lean chicken with parsnips and low-GI nuts with corn flakes.

Low-GI Foods – below 55

Fruit and Fruit Juices

Cherries	22
Grapefruit	25
Dried apricots	31
Pears	37
Apples	38
Plums	39
Apple juice	41
Peaches	42
Oranges	44
Grapes	46
Pineapple juice	46
Grapefruit juice	48
Orange juice	52
Kiwi fruit	53
Banana	54

Vegetables

Broccoli	10
Cabbage	10
Lettuce	10
Mushrooms	10
Raw onions	10
Raw red peppers	10
Raw carrots	49
Sweet potatoes	54

Grains

Pearl barley	31
Rye	34
Buckwheat	55
Brown basmati rice	52

Breads

Mixed grain bread	48
Pumpernickel rye bread	50

Pasta

Vermicelli	35
Linguine	42
Instant noodles	47

Bakery Products

Sponge cake (made with egg)	46

Breakfast Cereals

Bran cereal	42

Dairy

Low-fat yogurt	14
Full-fat milk	27
Skimmed milk	27
Low-fat fruit yogurt	33
Custard	43

Legumes

Soya beans	14
Red split lentils	18
Green lentils	29
Canned chickpeas	42
Canned pinto beans	45
Canned baked beans	48
Green peas	48

Medium-GI Foods – 55–70

Fruit and Fruit Juices

Mangoes	56
Sultanas	56
Apricots	57
Raisins	64
Pineapple	66
Watermelon	72

Vegetables

Sweetcorn	55
New potatoes	57
Beetroot	64
Boiled or mashed potatoes	70

Grains

Brown rice	55
White basmati rice	58

Breads

White pitta bread	58
Hamburger bun	61
Rye flour bread	64
High-fibre wheat bread	68
Wholemeal wheat bread	69

Pasta

Durum wheat spaghetti	55

Bakery Products

Pastry	59
Muffins	62
Croissant	67
Crumpet	69

Breakfast Cereals

Muesli	56
Porridge	61
Spun wheat biscuit	69

Biscuits

Oatmeal biscuits	55
Tea biscuits	55
Digestive biscuits	59
Shortbread	64

Savoury Biscuits

Wheat thins	67

Dairy

Ice cream	61

Legumes

Broad beans	79

Sugars

High-fruit jam	55
Honey	58
Table sugar	64

Sweets and Snacks

Popcorn	55

Beverages

Orange cordial	66
Fizzy orange	68

High-GI Foods – above 70

Vegetables

Swede	72
Chips	75
Pumpkin	75
Baked potatoes	85
Cooked carrots	85
Parsnips	97

Grains

White rice	88

Breads

White bagel	72
White wheat bread	78
Gluten-free bread	90
French baguette	95

Bakery Products

Doughnuts	76
Waffles	76

Breakfast Cereals

Wheat biscuits	70
Wheat bran flakes with added dried fruit	71
Puffed wheat	74
Crisped rice	82
Corn flakes	83

Savoury Biscuits and Crackers

Water biscuits	71
Rice cakes	77
Puffed crispbread	81

Sweets and Snacks

Corn tortillas	74
Jelly beans	80
Pretzels	81
Dates	99

Beverages

High-glucose sports drinks	95

This approach has been used in the book to create low- and medium-GI recipes that might still contain high-GI foods but do not raise blood-sugar levels beyond the 'normal' range by combining for average scores. You will see from the table that some 'treat' foods such as ice cream and biscuits have surprisingly low GI scores, but this is often due to their high fat content and they should still be eaten sparingly.

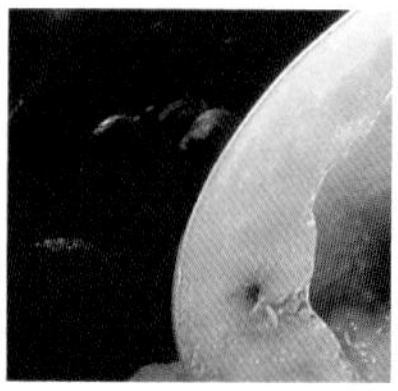

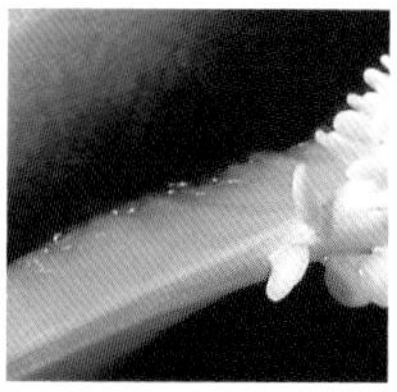

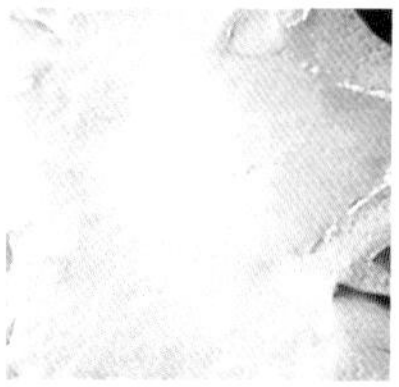

General Dietary Advice

For people with diabetes, the emphasis should be on consuming as much raw fruit and vegetables and fresh vegetable juices as possible where practical. This ensures a slow release of sugar into the bloodstream and the intake of as much insoluble fibre and the most nutrient-dense foods as possible.

The mineral chromium helps make a substance called Glucose Tolerance Factor (GTF) in the body, and aids the function of insulin and consequently the uptake of sugar by cells. This is therefore of particular importance to people with diabetes and may help those with Type II to increase insulin sensitivity. It is found in wholemeal bread, rye bread, potatoes, green peppers, eggs, chicken and apples.

Foods that contain nutrients needed for blood-sugar balance (zinc, magnesium, vitamins B_3, B_6 and C) are nuts, seeds, fish, dark green vegetables, brassicas (broccoli, cabbage, cauliflower, kale), pulses, beans, peas, eggs, avocados, oats, red/yellow/orange fruit, onions and asparagus. These foods are also important for managing cholesterol levels and lowering the risk of heart disease – which are important considerations for people with diabetes.

Avoiding stimulants (caffeine, alcohol and cigarettes) helps to eliminate the 'highs and lows' of blood sugar and reduce sugar cravings.

Reducing the Risk of Associated Conditions

Changing what and how you eat can reduce the risk of the diseases associated with diabetes such as neuropathies, kidney damage and retinopathy. These can occur when excess sugars in the blood harden. High blood pressure is also a concern for diabetics, and although diet can play a part here, it is important to emphasize how exercise and weight management can increase the benefits of a good diet. Exercising little and often – even daily walking – can have a more profound effect on circulation and these conditions than short, intermittent bursts of activity.

Foods that increase circulation such as dark and brightly coloured vegetables (whose pigments contain beneficial plant chemicals) and sulphur foods such as onions, garlic, eggs, broccoli, fennel, beans and pulses are also good for blood-sugar control. Vitamin C foods, specifically Brussels sprouts, blackcurrants, parsley, kale, Savoy cabbage, broccoli, peppers, tomatoes, kiwi fruit, orange juice, mangoes, cauliflower, mangetout, peas and sweet potatoes, help to prevent the incidence of secondary conditions and protect the body from damage. All the aforementioned foods also contain different vitamins and plant chemicals, especially carotenoids which protect fatty areas of the body that tend to get damaged in people with diabetes – the eyes, kidneys, liver and circulation from the heart.

It must also be pointed out that people with diabetes who smoke are two to three times more likely to develop kidney damage, according to research carried out at Colorado University Health Sciences Center, because smoking constricts the blood vessels.

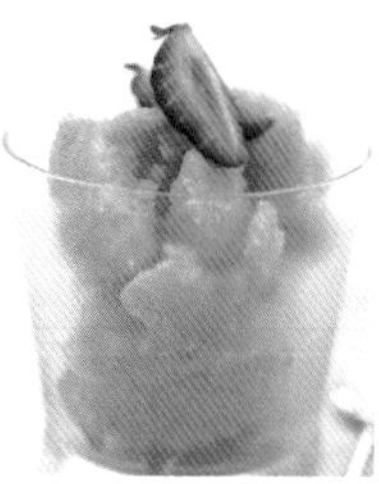

About the Recipes

When putting together the recipes in this book, practicality and ease were important factors. Choices were made to provide you with an accessible diet and versions of familiar recipes more beneficial to someone with diabetes. The overall GI score of combinations of foods was considered and a rating of either low or medium has been assigned to each recipe. It makes sense for you to prioritize those that are low and eat the medium ones less often. It is also important to vary your diet and the recipes to ensure a good spread of carbohydrates, fats and proteins. Check the nutritional information accompanying each recipe to help you obtain an overall diet that is low in fat and sugar and high in complex carbohydrates. When choosing recipes for one day, for instance, consider the balance of these macronutrients and try to obtain half of your daily calorie intake from carbohydrates, including snacks such as fruit.

A nutritional fact is also provided for each recipe which highlights the specific health benefits of certain foods for those with diabetes, for instance in balancing blood sugar, increasing the uptake of insulin, encouraging circulation to lower the risk of nerve damage, cleansing the body, lowering blood pressure and cholesterol levels and protecting against eye and kidney damage. Foods that are said to be of particular benefit to people with diabetes are blueberries, cinnamon, chicory, onion, pulses, beans, garlic, olive oil, nuts and avocados. These should be included in your diet often, but remember that a variety of foods is paramount to health, to ensure a full range and balance of nutrients.

The choice of specific varieties of ingredients used in the recipes also takes into account their effect on the release of blood sugar. For instance, if rice is featured in a recipe, brown basmati has been chosen as the best option. In the same way, consideration has been given to the choice of oils and types of fibre and carbohydrates, and this is reflected in the nutritional breakdowns.

Breakfasts & Brunches

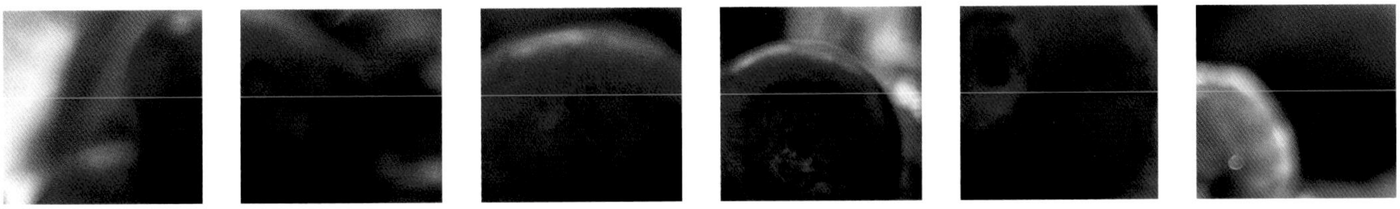

This chapter offers a selection of sweet and savoury dishes that should satisfy a healthy appetite while still being well balanced and delicious. All the dishes can be prepared relatively quickly. For a brunch party, you can think about offering a selection; for instance the Bircher Muesli or Greek Yogurt with Honey, Nuts & Blueberries, followed by Mexican Eggs and accompanied by Honey & Lemon Muffins.

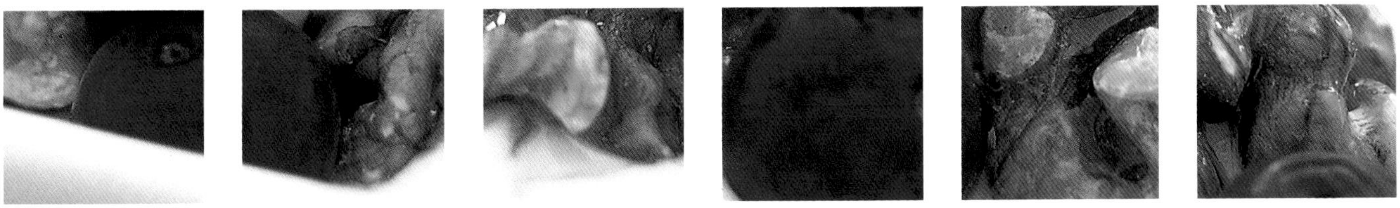

serves 4

Baked Eggs with Spinach

Ingredients
1 tbsp olive oil
3 shallots, finely chopped
500 g/1 lb 2 oz baby spinach leaves
4 tbsp single cream
freshly grated nutmeg
pepper
4 large eggs
4 tbsp Parmesan cheese, finely grated
toasted granary bread, to serve

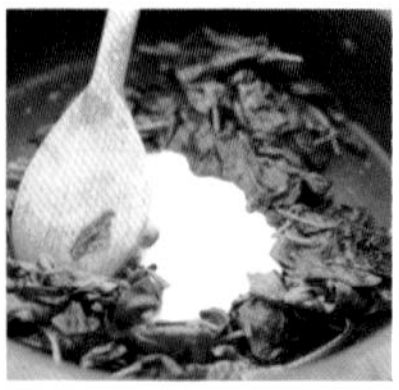
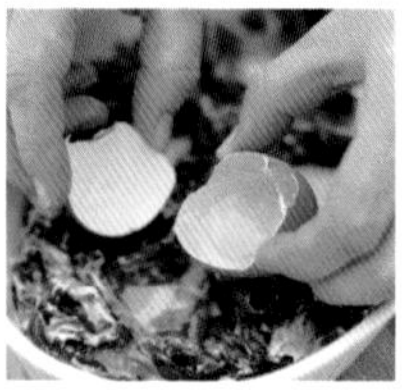

1 Preheat the oven to 200°C/400°F/Gas Mark 6. Heat the oil in a frying pan over a medium heat, add the shallots and cook, stirring frequently, for 4–5 minutes, or until soft. Add the spinach, cover and cook for 2–3 minutes, or until the spinach has wilted. Remove the lid and cook until all the liquid has evaporated.

2 Add the cream to the spinach and season to taste with nutmeg and pepper. Spread the spinach mixture over the base of a shallow gratin dish and make 4 wells in the mixture with the back of a spoon.

3 Crack an egg into each well and scatter over the cheese. Bake in the preheated oven for 12–15 minutes, or until the eggs are set. Serve with toasted Granary bread.

Nutritional Fact
Eggs contain lecithin, which helps to break down fats in the liver and improves sugar metabolism.

Serving Analysis

- *Calories* 185
- *Protein* 12g
- *Carbohydrate* 6.3g
- *Sugars* 1g
- *Fat* 13.3g
- *Saturates* 4.4g
- *GI* Low

makes 12

Honey & Lemon Muffins

Ingredients

- 50 g/1 3/4 oz unrefined caster sugar
- 25 g/1 oz unsalted butter, melted and cooled slightly
- 150 ml/5 fl oz buttermilk
- 2 eggs, beaten
- 4 tbsp clear flower honey
- finely grated rind of 1 lemon and juice of 1/2 lemon
- 225 g/8 oz plain flour
- 150 g/5 1/2 oz oat bran
- 1 1/2 tbsp baking powder

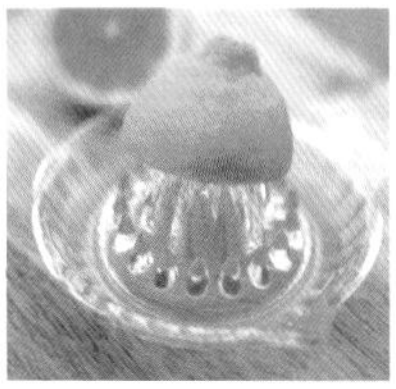

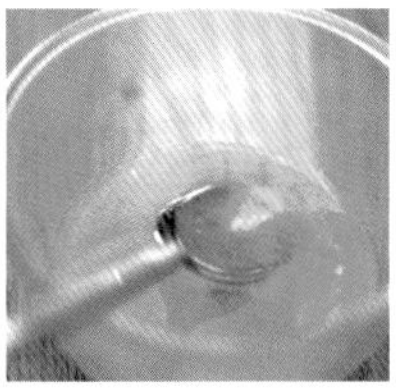

Nutritional Fact

Honey is just 58 on the Glycaemic Index, meaning it can be used very sparingly to sweeten foods.

Serving Analysis

• *Calories*	*165*
• *Protein*	*5.7g*
• *Carbohydrate*	*33g*
• *Sugars*	*10.8g*
• *Fat*	*3.7g*
• *Saturates*	*1.6g*
• *GI*	*Medium*

1 Preheat the oven to 180°C/350°F/Gas Mark 4. Line a 12-hole muffin tin with muffin paper cases.

2 Put the sugar into a jug and add the butter, buttermilk, eggs, half the honey and lemon rind. Mix briefly to combine.

3 Sift the flour into a large mixing bowl, add the oat bran and baking powder and stir to combine. Make a well in the centre of the flour mixture and add the buttermilk mixture. Quickly mix together – do not over-mix; the mixture should be slightly lumpy.

4 Spoon the mixture into the paper cases and bake in the preheated oven for 25 minutes. Turn out on to a wire rack.

5 Mix the lemon juice with the remaining honey in a small bowl or jug and drizzle over the muffins while they are still hot. Leave the muffins to stand for 10 minutes before serving.

serves 4

Greek Yogurt with Honey, Nuts & Blueberries

Nutritional Fact
Excellent for balancing blood sugar, blueberries are, therefore, a good food with which to begin the day.

Serving Analysis

• *Calories*	*239*
• *Protein*	*4.3g*
• *Carbohydrate*	*24g*
• *Sugars*	*19.4g*
• *Fat*	*15.6g*
• *Saturates*	*2.7g*
• *GI*	*Low*

1 Heat the honey in a small saucepan over a medium heat, add the nuts and stir until they are well coated. Remove from the heat and leave to cool slightly.

2 Divide the yogurt between 4 serving bowls, then spoon over the nut mixture and blueberries.

Ingredients

3 tbsp clear honey

100 g/3½ oz mixed unsalted nuts

8 tbsp Greek yogurt

200 g/7 oz fresh blueberries

serves 4

Mexican Eggs

Nutritional Fact

A good protein breakfast helps to sustain good blood-sugar levels throughout the day.

Serving Analysis

• *Calories*	*279*
• *Protein*	*15.8g*
• *Carbohydrate*	*4.9g*
• *Sugars*	*3.9g*
• *Fat*	*21.8g*
• *Saturates*	*6.3g*
• *GI*	*Low*

1 Beat the eggs, milk and pepper to taste in a large bowl. Set aside.

2 Heat the oil in a non-stick frying pan over a medium heat, add the red pepper and chilli and cook, stirring frequently, for 5 minutes, or until the red pepper is soft and browned in places. Add the chorizo and cook until just browned. Transfer to a warmed plate and set aside.

3 Return the pan to the heat, add the egg mixture and cook to a soft scramble. Add the chorizo mixture, stir to combine and scatter over the coriander. Serve immediately on toasted wholemeal bread.

Ingredients

- 8 large eggs
- 2 tbsp milk
- pepper
- 1 tsp olive oil
- 1 red pepper, deseeded and thinly sliced
- 1/2 fresh red chilli
- 1 fresh chorizo sausage, skinned and sliced
- 4 tbsp chopped fresh coriander
- 4 slices toasted wholemeal bread, to serve

serves 4

Baked Mushrooms

Ingredients

- 2 tbsp olive oil
- 8 field mushrooms
- 55 g/2 oz button mushrooms, finely chopped
- 2 garlic cloves, crushed
- 4 slices lean cooked ham, finely chopped
- 2 tbsp finely chopped fresh parsley
- pepper
- 4 slices rye bread, to serve

Nutritional Fact
Parsley is a good stress tonic that helps to keep blood-sugar levels manageable.

Serving Analysis

• *Calories*	*124*
• *Protein*	*6.6g*
• *Carbohydrate*	*4g*
• *Sugars*	*1.2g*
• *Fat*	*9.7g*
• *Saturates*	*0.8g*
• *GI*	*Low*

1 Preheat the oven to 190°/375°F/Gas Mark 5. Brush a baking sheet with a little of the oil. Arrange the field mushrooms, cup-side up, on the baking sheet.

2 Mix the button mushrooms, garlic, ham and parsley together in a bowl.

3 Divide the ham mixture between the field mushroom cups. Drizzle with the remaining oil and season to taste with pepper.

4 Bake in the preheated oven for 10 minutes, then serve immediately with rye bread.

serves 4

Onion & Gruyère Frittata

Ingredients

- 1 tbsp olive oil
- 1 garlic clove, crushed
- 2 red onions, thinly sliced
- 8 eggs
- 100 g/3½ oz Gruyère cheese, grated
- pepper
- 4 slices soda bread, to serve

1 Heat the oil in a non-stick frying pan over a medium–low heat, add the garlic and onions and cook, stirring occasionally, for 10 minutes, or until the onions are very soft and a little caramelized.

2 Beat the eggs with half the cheese and pepper to taste in a large bowl, pour over the onions and gently stir until the eggs are evenly distributed. Cook for 5 minutes, or until the eggs are set on the bottom.

3 Meanwhile, preheat the grill to high. Scatter the remaining cheese over the frittata and place under the preheated grill until the cheese is melted. Cut the frittata into 4 wedges and serve immediately with soda bread.

Nutritional Fact

Onions contain sulphur, which is good for the circulation and liver. Both are important for people with diabetes.

Serving Analysis

- *Calories* *304*
- *Protein* *20.6g*
- *Carbohydrate* *6.3g*
- *Sugars* *2.9g*
- *Fat* *21.7g*
- *Saturates* *7.9g*
- *GI* *Low*

serves 4

Bircher Muesli

Ingredients

- 150 g/5½ oz rolled oats
- 225 ml/8 fl oz apple juice
- 1 apple, grated
- 125 ml/4 fl oz natural yogurt
- 150 g/5½ oz blackberries
- 2 plums, stoned and sliced
- 2 tbsp clear honey

Nutritional Fact

Oats release their sugars very slowly, making them a good breakfast food.

Serving Analysis

- *Calories* *285*
- *Protein* *8.4g*
- *Carbohydrate* *56g*
- *Sugars* *25.5g*
- *Fat* *4.2g*
- *Saturates* *1.1g*
- *GI* *Low*

1 Put the oats and apple juice into a mixing bowl and combine well. Cover and refrigerate overnight.

2 To serve, stir the apple and yogurt into the soaked oats and divide between 4 serving bowls. Top with the blackberries and plums and drizzle with the honey.

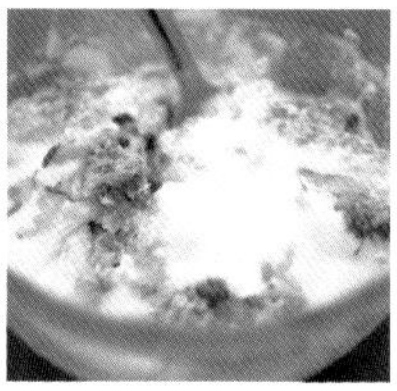

serves 4

Asparagus with Poached Eggs & Parmesan

Ingredients

300 g/$10\frac{1}{2}$ oz asparagus, trimmed
4 large eggs
85 g/3 oz Parmesan cheese
pepper

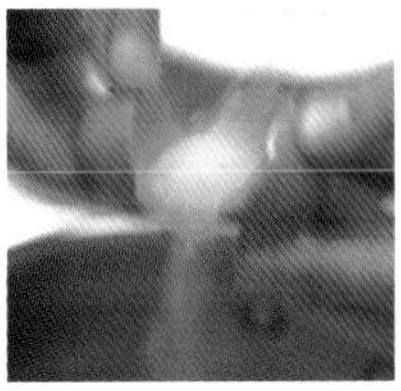

Nutritional Fact
Asparagus is known to be beneficial to the kidneys, which can be damaged if a person has diabetes.

Serving Analysis

- *Calories* 175
- *Protein* 15.6g
- *Carbohydrate* 4.7g
- *Sugars* 1.8g
- *Fat* 10.6g
- *Saturates* 5g
- *GI* Low

1 Bring 2 saucepans of water to the boil. Add the asparagus to 1 saucepan, return to a simmer and cook for 5 minutes, or until just tender.

2 Meanwhile, reduce the heat of the second saucepan to a simmer and carefully crack in the eggs, one at a time. Poach for 3 minutes, or until the whites are just set but the yolks are still soft. Remove with a slotted spoon.

3 Drain the asparagus and divide between 4 warmed plates. Top each plate of asparagus with an egg and shave over the cheese. Season to taste with pepper and serve immediately.

Soups & Light Meals

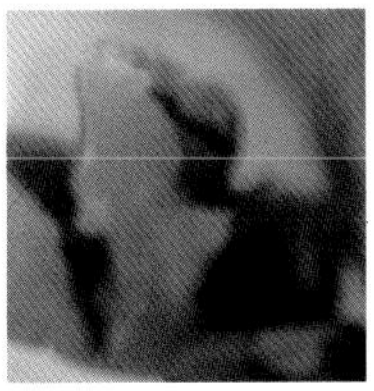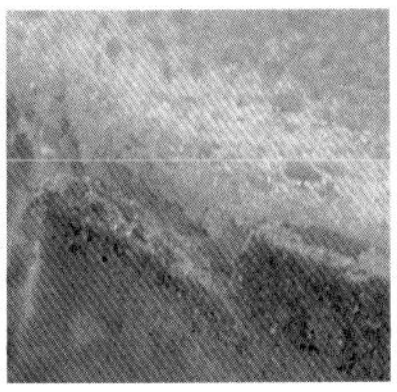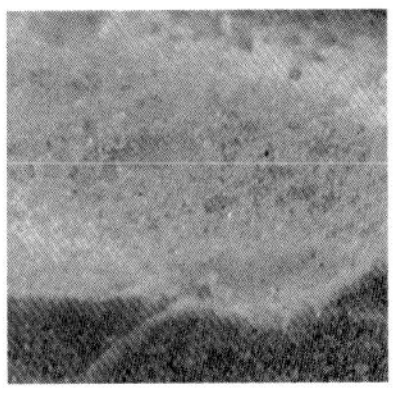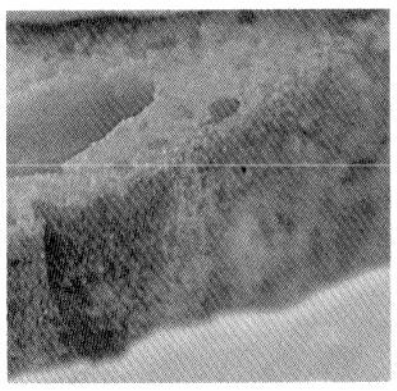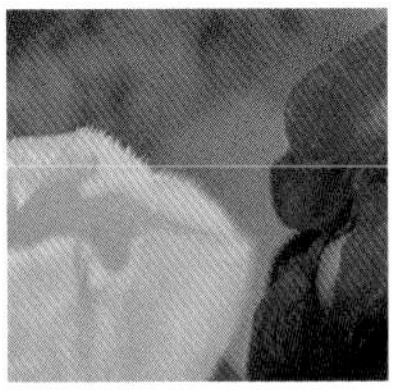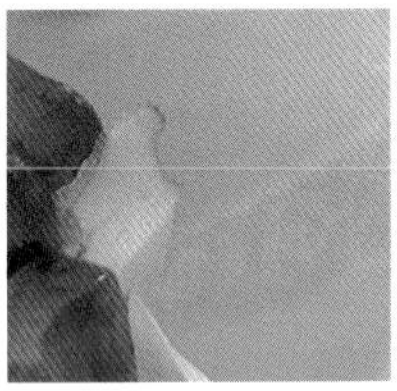

Eating a healthy diet doesn't mean sacrificing taste and variety, and the recipes in this chapter illustrate how to use ingredients and influences from around the world to produce sophisticated and tasty light dishes. These recipes are flexible since they can almost all be eaten as first courses for a dinner party as well as light lunches on their own. The Crab Cakes and Coconut Prawns would also make good party offerings.

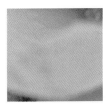

serves 4

Soup au Pistou

Ingredients

- 1 litre/$1^3/_4$ pints fresh cold water
- bouquet garni of 1 fresh parsley sprig, 1 fresh thyme sprig and 1 bay leaf, tied together with clean string
- 2 celery sticks, chopped
- 3 baby leeks, chopped
- 4 baby carrots, chopped
- 150 g/$5^1/_2$ oz new potatoes, scrubbed and cut into bite-sized chunks
- 4 tbsp shelled broad beans or peas
- 175 g/6 oz canned cannellini or flageolet beans, drained and rinsed
- 3 heads pak choi
- 150 g/$5^1/_2$ oz rocket
- pepper

For the pistou

- 2 large handfuls fresh basil leaves
- 1 fresh green chilli, deseeded
- 2 garlic cloves
- 4 tbsp olive oil
- 1 tsp Parmesan cheese, finely grated

1 Put the water and bouquet garni into a large saucepan and add the celery, leeks, carrots and potatoes. Bring to the boil, then reduce the heat and simmer for 10 minutes.

2 Stir in the broad beans or peas and canned beans and simmer for a further 10 minutes. Stir in the pak choi, rocket and pepper to taste and simmer for a further 2–3 minutes. Remove and discard the bouquet garni.

3 Meanwhile, to make the pistou, put the basil, chilli, garlic and oil into a food processor and pulse to form a thick paste. Stir in the cheese.

4 Stir most of the pistou into the soup, then ladle into warmed bowls. Top with the remaining pistou and serve immediately.

Nutritional Fact

Beans and pulses contain soluble fibre. This balances blood sugar and cleanses the body.

Serving Analysis

• *Calories*	*370*
• *Protein*	*19g*
• *Carbohydrate*	*46g*
• *Sugars*	*13.3g*
• *Fat*	*17g*
• *Saturates*	*0.6g*
• *GI*	*Medium*

serves 4

Chicken with Linguine & Artichokes

Ingredients

4 chicken breasts, skinned

finely grated rind and juice of 1 lemon

2 tbsp olive oil

2 garlic cloves, crushed

400 g/14 oz canned artichoke hearts, drained and sliced

250 g/9 oz baby plum tomatoes

300 g/10½ oz dried linguine

To serve

chopped fresh parsley

Parmesan cheese, finely grated

Nutritional Fact

Artichokes contain cynarin, which helps lower cholesterol. Cholesterol levels can rise when blood-sugar levels fluctuate.

Serving Analysis

- *Calories* 534
- *Protein* 41g
- *Carbohydrate* 66g
- *Sugars* 2.9g
- *Fat* 10g
- *Saturates* 0.03g
- *GI* Medium

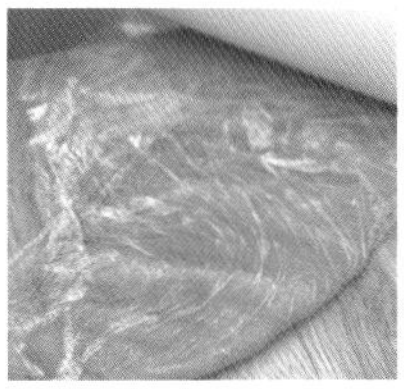

1 Put each chicken breast in turn between 2 pieces of clingfilm and bash with a rolling pin to flatten. Put the chicken into a shallow, non-metallic dish with the lemon rind and juice and 1 tablespoon of the oil and turn to coat in the marinade. Cover and leave to marinate in the refrigerator for 30 minutes.

2 Put a large saucepan of water on to boil. Heat the remaining oil in a frying pan over a low heat, add the garlic and cook for 1 minute, stirring frequently. Add the artichokes and tomatoes and cook for 5 minutes, stirring occasionally. Add about half the marinade from the chicken and cook over a medium heat for a further 5 minutes.

3 Meanwhile, preheat the grill to high. Remove the chicken from the remaining marinade and arrange on the grill pan. Cook the chicken under the preheated grill for 5 minutes each side until thoroughly cooked through. Meanwhile, add the linguine to the boiling water and cook for 7–9 minutes, or until just tender.

4 Drain the pasta and return to the saucepan, pour over the artichoke and tomato mixture and slice in the cooked chicken.

5 Divide between 4 warmed plates and scatter over the parsley and cheese.

serves 4

Hot & Sour Soup with Tofu

Nutritional Fact

Ginger and garlic are good for the circulation, and vegetable protein is a better choice than meat protein for a diet with a low saturated-fat content.

Serving Analysis

• *Calories*	*353*
• *Protein*	*17g*
• *Carbohydrate*	*44g*
• *Sugars*	*2.7g*
• *Fat*	*12.8g*
• *Saturates*	*2g*
• *GI*	*Low*

Ingredients

- 3 strips of rind and juice of 1 lime
- 2 garlic cloves, peeled
- 2 slices fresh root ginger
- 1 litre/1 3/4 pints low-salt chicken stock
- 1 tbsp vegetable oil
- 150 g/5 1/2 oz firm tofu (drained weight), cubed
- 200 g/7 oz dried fine egg noodles
- 100 g/3 1/2 oz shiitake mushrooms, sliced
- 1 fresh red chilli, deseeded and sliced
- 4 spring onions, sliced
- 1 tsp low-salt soy sauce
- 1 tsp Chinese rice wine
- 1 tsp sesame oil
- chopped fresh coriander, to garnish

1 Put the lime rind, garlic and ginger into a large saucepan with the stock and bring to the boil. Reduce the heat and simmer for 5 minutes. Remove the lime rind, garlic and ginger with a slotted spoon and discard.

2 Meanwhile, heat the vegetable oil in a large frying pan over a high heat, add the tofu and cook, turning frequently, until golden. Remove from the pan and drain on kitchen paper.

3 Add the noodles, mushrooms and chilli to the stock and simmer for 3 minutes. Add the tofu, spring onions, soy sauce, lime juice, rice wine and sesame oil and briefly heat through.

4 Divide the soup between 4 warmed bowls, scatter over the coriander and serve immediately.

makes 12

Crab Cakes with Dipping Sauce

Ingredients

For the crab cakes

- 4 spring onions
- 300 g/10½ oz raw prawns, peeled and deveined
- 300 g/10½ oz cooked white crabmeat
- 1 tsp finely chopped capers
- 2 tsp chopped fresh dill
- white pepper
- 1 small egg, lightly beaten
- 1 tsp Dijon mustard
- 1 tbsp plain flour, plus extra for flouring
- vegetable oil, for frying

For the dipping sauce

- 2 tbsp finely chopped fresh root ginger
- 6 tbsp low-salt soy sauce
- 3 tbsp clear honey
- juice of 1 lime
- 2 tbsp sesame oil

1 First make the dipping sauce. Put the ginger, soy sauce and honey into a small saucepan and simmer for 3 minutes. Remove from the heat and stir in the lime juice and sesame oil. Set aside. Transfer to a small serving dish when cool.

2 Put the spring onions into a food processor and pulse to chop finely. Add the prawns, crabmeat and capers and process to combine. Turn into a bowl and mix in the dill, pepper to taste, egg, mustard and flour.

3 With floured hands, shape the mixture into 12 cakes and put on a large plate. Cover and chill in the refrigerator for 1 hour.

4 Heat a little vegetable oil in a large frying pan over a medium heat. Cook the crab cakes, in batches, for 3–4 minutes on each side. Remove from the pan with a slotted spoon and drain on kitchen paper. Keep the crab cakes hot while cooking the remainder.

5 Serve the crab cakes hot with the dipping sauce.

Nutritional Fact

Fish is packed with protein, but low in saturated fat. It helps stabilize blood-sugar levels and protect against stress. All the sugar here is in the dip; each crab cake is practically sugar-free.

Serving Analysis

• *Calories*	*111*
• *Protein*	*11.4g*
• *Carbohydrate*	*6.6g*
• *Sugars*	*4.7g*
• *Fat*	*4.5g*
• *Saturates*	*0.7g*
• *GI*	*Low*

serves 4

Trout Fillets with Lime, Sesame & Chilli

Ingredients

- 2 tbsp sesame seeds
- 250 ml/9 fl oz fish stock
- 8 trout fillets, about 150 g/5 1/2 oz each
- 250 g/9 oz dried fine egg noodles
- juice of 1/2 lime
- 1 fresh red chilli, deseeded and thinly sliced
- 1 tbsp sesame oil, plus extra for drizzling
- 1 tbsp vegetable oil
- 1 tsp Thai fish sauce

To serve

- 1 bunch watercress
- 4 lime wedges

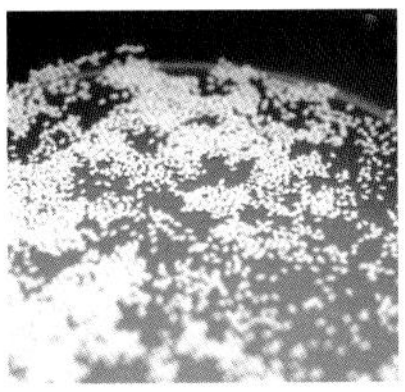

Nutritional Fact

Trout contains good levels of essential fatty acids. These are the good fats that can help stabilize blood-sugar levels.

Serving Analysis

- *Calories* 563
- *Protein* 45g
- *Carbohydrate* 48g
- *Sugars* 1.4g
- *Fat* 19.5g
- *Saturates* 3.7g
- *GI* Low

1 Heat a non-stick frying pan over a medium heat, add the sesame seeds and cook, turning, until they begin to colour. Tip on to a plate and set aside.

2 Put the stock into a large frying pan and bring to a simmer. Add the trout fillets and poach gently for 7–10 minutes, or until just cooked.

3 Meanwhile, bring a large saucepan of water to the boil, add the noodles and cook for 3 minutes. Drain and toss with the sesame seeds, lime juice, chilli, oils and fish sauce. Keep warm.

4 To serve, pile an equal quantity of noodles on each of 4 serving plates and top with 2 trout fillets, some watercress and a lime wedge. Drizzle with a little more sesame oil.

serves 4

Tuscan Bean Soup

Ingredients

- 1 tbsp olive oil
- 4 slices pancetta or thin-cut bacon rashers, diced
- 2 garlic cloves, crushed
- 1 large red onion, thinly sliced
- 800 g/1 lb 12 oz canned cannellini beans, drained and rinsed
- 1 fresh rosemary sprig
- 1 litre/1 3/4 pints low-salt chicken or vegetable stock
- pepper

To garnish

- olive oil
- chopped fresh parsley

1 Heat the oil in a large saucepan over a medium heat, add the pancetta and cook for 1–2 minutes, stirring frequently. Add the garlic and onion and cook for 10 minutes, stirring occasionally, until the onion is soft and translucent.

2 Add the beans, rosemary and stock and simmer over a low heat for 15 minutes.

3 Remove and discard the rosemary. Leave the soup to cool slightly, then transfer, in small batches, to a food processor or blender and process until blended but not entirely smooth. Return to a clean saucepan and gently heat through. Season to taste with pepper.

4 Serve in warmed bowls drizzled with oil and scattered with parsley.

Nutritional Fact

Adding rosemary to cooking helps to prevent the damaging effects of heating fats.

Serving Analysis

- *Calories* — *334*
- *Protein* — *24g*
- *Carbohydrate* — *40g*
- *Sugars* — *3.7g*
- *Fat* — *7.6g*
- *Saturates* — *1.2g*
- *GI* — *Low*

serves 4

Chicory & Walnut Salad with Goat's Cheese & Pomegranate Seeds

Ingredients
400 g/14 oz chicory
100 g/3½ oz walnut pieces
seeds from 1 pomegranate
2 tbsp walnut oil
2 tsp red wine vinegar
1 tsp Dijon mustard
pepper
4 slices granary bread
2 garlic cloves, halved
4 x 100-g/3½-oz goat's cheeses, with rind
3 tsp olive oil

Nutritional Fact

Chicory contains inulin, a natural fructose that helps people with diabetes to lower insulin levels.

Serving Analysis

• *Calories*	*779*
• *Protein*	*33g*
• *Carbohydrate*	*29g*
• *Sugars*	*3.2g*
• *Fat*	*62g*
• *Saturates*	*24g*
• *GI*	*Low*

1 Divide the heads of chicory into leaves and rinse, pat dry with kitchen paper and arrange on 4 serving plates. Scatter over the walnut pieces and pomegranate seeds.

2 To make the dressing, whisk the walnut oil with the vinegar and mustard in a small bowl. Season with pepper and set aside.

3 Preheat the grill to high. Rub the bread with the garlic. Arrange the goat's cheeses on a sheet of foil and place on the grill pan with the bread alongside. Cook under the preheated grill until the bread is toasted on both sides and the cheese is bubbling.

4 To serve, drizzle each toasted bread slice with the olive oil and top with a goat's cheese. Put one goat's cheese toast on each salad and drizzle the whole dish with the dressing.

serves 4

Coconut Prawns with Cucumber Salad

1 Bring a large saucepan of water to the boil, add the rice and cook for 25 minutes, or until tender. Drain and keep in a colander covered with a clean tea towel to absorb the steam.

2 Meanwhile, soak 8 wooden skewers in cold water for 30 minutes, then drain.

3 Crush the coriander seeds in a mortar with a pestle. Heat a non-stick frying pan over a medium heat, add the crushed coriander seeds and cook, turning, until they begin to colour. Tip on to a plate and set aside.

4 Put the egg whites into a shallow bowl and the coconut into a separate bowl. Roll each prawn first in the egg whites, then in the coconut. Thread on to a skewer. Repeat so that each skewer is threaded with 3 coated prawns.

5 Preheat the grill to high. Using a potato peeler, peel long strips from the cucumber to create ribbons, put into a colander to drain, then toss with the spring onions and oil in a bowl and set aside.

6 Cook the prawns under the preheated grill for 3–4 minutes on each side, or until pink and slightly browned.

7 Meanwhile, mix the rice with the toasted coriander seeds and fresh coriander and press into 4 dariole moulds or individual ramekins. Invert each mould on to a serving plate and divide the cucumber salad between the plates. Serve with the hot prawn skewers, garnished with lime wedges.

Ingredients

- 200 g/7 oz brown basmati rice
- 1/2 tsp coriander seeds
- 2 egg whites, lightly beaten
- 100 g/3 1/2 oz unsweetened desiccated coconut
- 24 raw tiger prawns, peeled and tails left intact
- 1/2 cucumber
- 4 spring onions, thinly sliced lengthways
- 1 tsp sesame oil
- 1 tbsp finely chopped fresh coriander
- 1 lime, cut into wedges, to garnish

Nutritional Fact

Brown basmati rice is a great stabilizer of blood-sugar levels and helps to keep down sugar cravings.

Serving Analysis

- *Calories* — *412*
- *Protein* — *16g*
- *Carbohydrate* — *47g*
- *Sugars* — *3.1g*
- *Fat* — *19g*
- *Saturates* — *14.6g*
- *GI* — *Low*

Seafood, Meat & Poultry

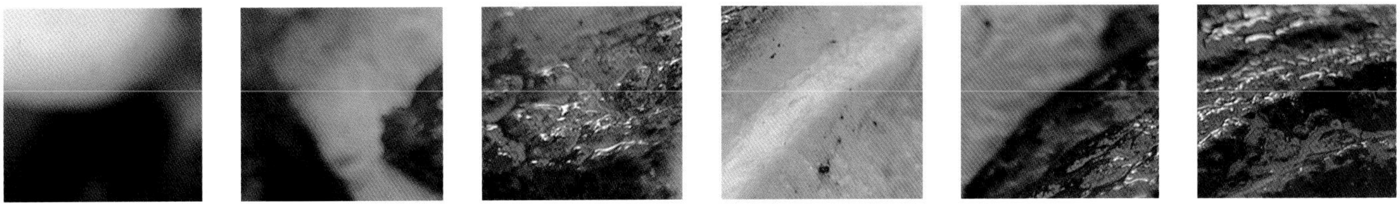

This chapter offers quick suppers, easy to prepare if you're in a hurry, and one-pot dishes slow-cooked to maximize flavour. Remember that, although protein is an important part of any balanced diet, it's important to choose lean cuts of meat and to make the most of the variety of fish and fowl available to vary your diet. Also, make sure you include lots of fresh vegetables and beans or pulses.

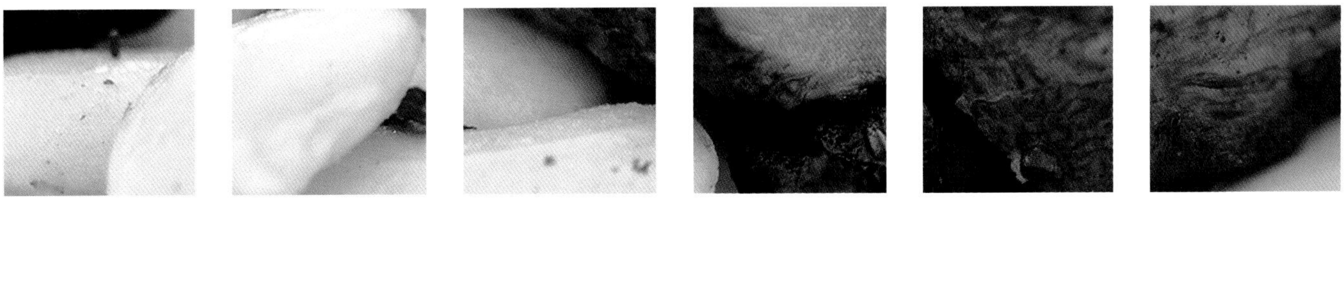

serves 4

Ginger-marinated Salmon & Scallops

Ingredients

200 g/7 oz brown basmati rice

1/2 cucumber, diced

4 spring onions, sliced

1/2 bunch fresh coriander, chopped

1 red pepper, deseeded and diced

1 fresh green chilli, deseeded and thinly sliced

juice of 1 lime

2 tbsp toasted sesame oil

500 g/1 lb 2 oz salmon fillet, skinned and cut into chunks

8 scallops, without corals, cleaned

50 g/1 3/4 oz fresh root ginger

juice of 1 lemon

1 tbsp olive oil

green salad, to serve

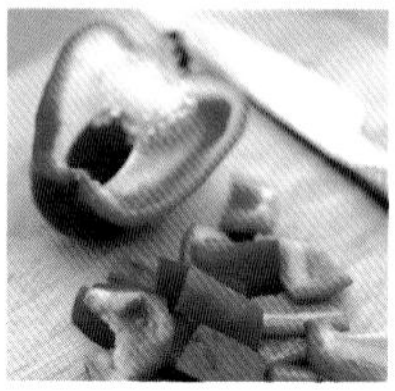

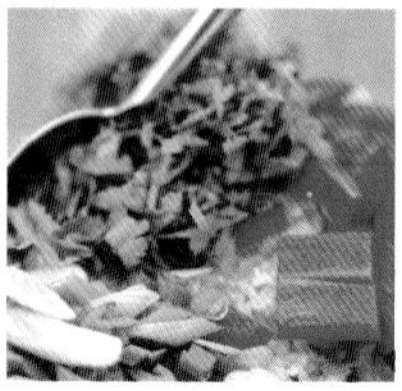

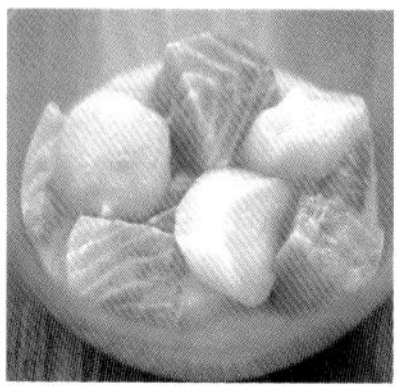

Nutritional Fact

Salmon is high in essential fatty acids, which are good fats that help stabilize blood-sugar levels.

Serving Analysis

- *Calories* *559*
- *Protein* *34g*
- *Carbohydrate* *47g*
- *Sugars* *3.1g*
- *Fat* *26g*
- *Saturates* *3.8g*
- *GI* *Low*

1 Bring a large saucepan of water to the boil, add the rice and cook for 25 minutes, or until tender. Drain and leave to cool. Mix the cooled rice with the cucumber, spring onions, coriander, red pepper, chilli, lime juice and sesame oil in a bowl. Cover and set aside for the flavours to develop.

2 Meanwhile, put the salmon chunks into a shallow, non-metallic bowl. Cut each scallop in half and add to the bowl. Using a garlic press or the back of a knife, crush the ginger to extract the juice. Mix the ginger juice with the lemon juice and olive oil in a small bowl or jug and pour over the seafood. Turn the seafood to coat in the marinade. Cover and leave to marinate in the refrigerator for 30 minutes. Soak 8 wooden skewers in cold water for 30 minutes, then drain.

3 Preheat the grill to high. Thread an equal quantity of the salmon and scallops on to the skewers. Cook under the preheated grill for 3–4 minutes on each side, or until cooked through.

4 Serve the hot seafood skewers with the rice salad and a green salad.

serves 4

Tuna & Avocado Salad

Ingredients

- 2 avocados, stoned, peeled and cubed
- 250 g/9 oz cherry tomatoes, halved
- 2 red peppers, deseeded and chopped
- 1 bunch fresh flat-leaved parsley, chopped
- 2 garlic cloves, crushed
- 1 fresh red chilli, deseeded and finely chopped
- juice of 1/2 lemon
- 6 tbsp olive oil
- pepper
- 3 tbsp sesame seeds
- 4 fresh tuna steaks, about 150 g/5 1/2 oz each
- 8 cooked new potatoes, cubed
- rocket leaves, to serve

1 Toss the avocados, tomatoes, red peppers, parsley, garlic, chilli, lemon juice and 2 tablespoons of the oil together in a large bowl. Season to taste with pepper, cover and chill in the refrigerator for 30 minutes.

2 Lightly crush the sesame seeds in a mortar with a pestle. Tip the crushed seeds on to a plate and spread out. Press each tuna steak in turn into the crushed seeds to coat on both sides.

3 Heat 2 tablespoons of the remaining oil in a frying pan, add the potatoes and cook, stirring frequently, for 5–8 minutes, or until crisp and brown. Remove from the pan and drain on kitchen paper.

4 Wipe out the pan, add the remaining oil and heat over a high heat until very hot. Add the tuna steaks and cook for 3–4 minutes on each side.

5 To serve, divide the avocado salad between 4 serving plates. Top each with a tuna steak, then scatter over the potatoes and a handful of rocket leaves.

Nutritional Fact

Avocados are rich in nutrients that can help to protect the eyes against diabetes-related damage.

Serving Analysis

- *Calories* 785
- *Protein* 44g
- *Carbohydrate* 57g
- *Sugars* 7.1g
- *Fat* 46g
- *Saturates* 3g
- *GI* Low

serves 4

Sardines Escabechadas

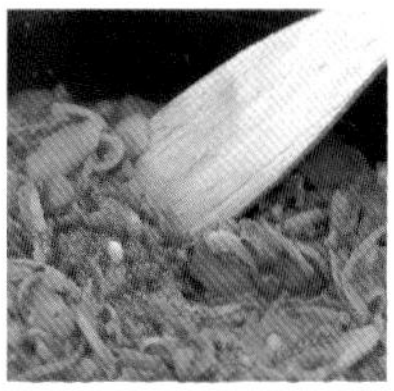

Ingredients

- 1 kg/2 lb 4 oz fresh sardines, cleaned and scaled
- 2 tbsp plain flour
- 100 ml/3½ fl oz olive oil, plus 2 tbsp
- 1 large onion, sliced
- 2 garlic cloves, thinly sliced
- 1 small carrot, scraped and thinly sliced
- 2 tbsp chopped fresh parsley
- 1 tsp chopped fresh oregano
- 1 tsp ground cumin
- pepper
- 1 tsp sugar
- 4 tbsp red wine vinegar
- 400 g/14 oz canned chopped tomatoes
- 250 g/9 oz brown basmati rice
- 50 g/1¾ oz chopped mixed fresh herbs
- 50 g/1¾ oz chopped almonds

Nutritional Fact

Sardines provide beneficial fats, and onion and garlic help to balance blood sugar.

Serving Analysis

- *Calories* 1145
- *Protein* 56g
- *Carbohydrate* 66g
- *Sugars* 10.2g
- *Fat* 74.5g
- *Saturates* 8.7g
- *GI* Medium

1 Preheat the oven to 160°C/325°F/Gas Mark 3. Rinse the sardines and pat dry with kitchen paper. Spread the flour out on a plate. Roll each fish in the flour to coat.

2 Heat 50 ml/2 fl oz of the oil in a large frying pan over a high heat, add the fish, in batches, and cook briefly on both sides until golden. Transfer to a large, shallow, ovenproof dish.

3 Heat the remaining oil (excluding the 2 tablespoons) in the frying pan over a medium heat, add the onion and garlic and cook, stirring frequently, for 5 minutes, or until softened. Add the carrot and cook for a further 5 minutes. Stir in the parsley, oregano, cumin, pepper to taste, sugar, vinegar and tomatoes and simmer for 15 minutes. Pour the sauce over the sardines and bake in the preheated oven for 15 minutes.

4 Meanwhile, bring a large saucepan of water to the boil, add the rice and cook for 25 minutes, or until tender. Drain, transfer to a warmed serving dish and mix with the herbs, almonds, the 2 tablespoons of oil and pepper to taste. Serve the rice hot with the fish.

serves 4

Roast Beef Salad

Ingredients

- 750 g/1lb 10oz beef fillet, trimmed of any visible fat
- pepper, to taste
- 2 tsp Worcestershire sauce
- 3 tbsp olive oil
- 400 g/14 oz green beans
- 100 g/3½ oz small pasta, such as orecchiette
- 2 red onions, finely sliced
- 1 large head radicchio
- 50 g/1¾ oz green olives, stoned
- 50 g/1¾ oz shelled hazelnuts, whole

For the dressing

- 1 tsp Dijon mustard
- 2 tbsp white wine vinegar
- 5 tbsp olive oil

Nutritional Fact

This recipe has a good mix of protein, fibre, beans and onions, making it a good dish for stablizing blood-sugar levels.

Serving Analysis

• *Calories*	*748*
• *Protein*	*46g*
• *Carbohydrate*	*32g*
• *Sugars*	*7g*
• *Fat*	*51g*
• *Saturates*	*6g*
• *GI*	*Low*

1 Preheat the oven to 220°C/425°F/Gas Mark 7. Rub the beef with pepper to taste and Worcestershire sauce. Heat 2 tablespoons of the oil in a small roasting tin over a high heat, add the beef and sear on all sides. Transfer the dish to the preheated oven and roast for 30 minutes. Remove and leave to cool.

2 Bring a large saucepan of water to the boil, add the beans and cook for 5 minutes, or until just tender. Remove with a slotted spoon and refresh the beans under cold running water. Drain and put into a large bowl.

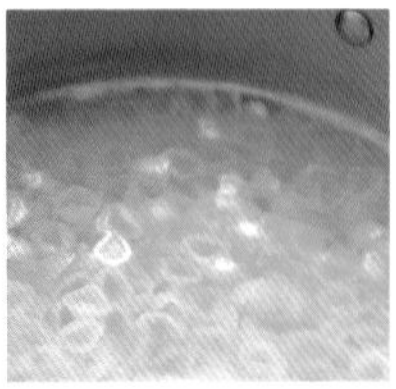

3 Return the bean cooking water to the boil, add the pasta and cook for 11 minutes, or until tender. Drain, return to the saucepan and toss with the remaining oil.

4 Add the pasta to the beans with the onions, radicchio leaves, olives and hazelnuts in a serving dish or salad bowl and arrange some thinly sliced beef on top.

5 Whisk the dressing ingredients together in a separate bowl, then pour over the salad and serve immediately with extra sliced beef.

serves 4

Lamb with Rosemary, Potatoes, Peppers & Tomato

1 Preheat the oven to 180°C/350°F/Gas Mark 4. Wipe the meat with kitchen paper and dust with the flour. Heat half the oil in a flameproof casserole dish over a medium heat. Add the meat, in batches, and brown on all sides. Remove from the casserole dish with a slotted spoon and keep warm.

2 Heat the remaining oil in the casserole dish over a medium heat, add the onions and garlic and cook, stirring frequently, for 5 minutes, or until lightly browned. Add the rosemary, then gradually add the stock, stirring constantly.

3 Return the meat to the casserole dish and add the potatoes, tomatoes, red peppers, orange rind and pepper to taste. Bring up to a simmer, stirring constantly. Cover and cook in the preheated oven for $1^1/_2$ hours, stirring occasionally. Remove and discard the orange rind before serving.

Ingredients

- 900 g/2 lb lean lamb, cubed
- 1 tbsp plain flour
- 2 tbsp olive oil
- 2 onions, sliced
- 2 garlic cloves, sliced
- 2 fresh rosemary sprigs
- 500 ml/18 fl oz lamb stock
- 8 small potatoes
- 250 g/9 oz cherry tomatoes
- 2 red peppers, deseeded and sliced
- 2 pieces orange rind
- pepper

Nutritional Fact

Lycopene, found in tomatoes and peppers, is an antioxidant that protects against damage from high insulin levels.

Serving Analysis

- *Calories* 861
- *Protein* 46
- *Carbohydrate* 56g
- *Sugars* 7.8g
- *Fat* 50g
- *Saturates* 18.3g
- *GI* Medium

serves 4

Duck with Refried Beans, Olives & Thyme

Ingredients

4 duck breasts, skin on

3 garlic cloves, crushed

1 tbsp finely chopped fresh thyme

2 tbsp olive oil

800 g/1 lb 12 oz canned butter beans, drained and rinsed

12 black olives, stoned and sliced

pepper

rocket and watercress salad, to serve

Nutritional Fact
Garlic helps to lower blood pressure and cholesterol levels.

Serving Analysis

• *Calories*	*497*
• *Protein*	*18g*
• *Carbohydrate*	*31g*
• *Sugars*	*1.6g*
• *Fat*	*38g*
• *Saturates*	*9.7g*
• *GI*	*Low*

1 Wipe the duck breasts with kitchen paper and slash the skin across the breasts in several places. Rub half the garlic and the thyme into the cuts.

2 Heat the oil in a frying pan over a low heat, add the remaining garlic and cook for 1 minute, stirring frequently. Add the beans and cook for 5 minutes. Add the olives and cook for a further 5 minutes, or until the edges of the beans become golden and crusty. Season to taste with pepper.

3 Meanwhile, preheat the grill to medium. Arrange the duck breasts, skin-side up, on the grill pan. Cook under the preheated grill for 5 minutes on each side for medium, or add a further 3–5 minutes to the total cooking time for well done. Remove from the grill and cut each breast into slices.

4 To serve, pile the beans on to 4 warmed serving plates and top with the sliced duck. Serve with a rocket and watercress salad.

serves 4

Roast Cinnamon Poussins with Spiced Lentils

Ingredients

- 4 poussins, about 500 g/1 lb 2 oz each
- 2 tbsp maple syrup
- 1 tsp ground cinnamon
- 1 tbsp vegetable oil
- 100 ml/3½ fl oz low-salt chicken stock
- 2 red onions, sliced
- 1 tsp cumin seeds
- 1 tsp coriander seeds
- 1 tbsp olive oil
- 2 garlic cloves, crushed
- 800 g/1 lb 12 oz canned lentils, drained and rinsed
- 1 tbsp unsalted butter
- 2 tbsp chopped fresh parsley
- pepper
- steamed broccoli or green beans, to serve

1 Preheat the oven to 190°C/375°F/Gas Mark 5. Arrange the poussins in a roasting tin. Mix the maple syrup, cinnamon and vegetable oil together in a small bowl and brush over the breasts of the poussins. Pour the stock into the roasting tin and tuck the onion slices around the birds. Roast the poussins in the preheated oven for 35 minutes.

2 Meanwhile, heat a non-stick frying pan over a medium heat, add the cumin and coriander seeds and cook, turning, until they begin to give off an aroma. Tip into a mortar and finely crush with a pestle.

3 Heat the olive oil in a frying pan over a low heat, add the garlic and spices and cook for 1–2 minutes, stirring constantly. Add the lentils and cook for 10–15 minutes, stirring occasionally.

4 When the birds are cooked, remove from the oven, transfer to a warmed plate and keep warm. Put the roasting tin on the hob and bring the cooking juices up to a simmer. Stir in the butter and half the parsley. Season to taste with pepper.

5 To serve, divide the lentils between 4 warmed serving plates. Add a poussin to each plate, pour over the sauce and scatter with the remaining parsley. Serve with steamed broccoli or green beans.

Nutritional Fact

One teaspoon of cinnamon a day has proved to be useful for controlling Type II diabetes.

Serving Analysis

- *Calories* 769
- *Protein* 87g
- *Carbohydrate* 53g
- *Sugars* 13.4g
- *Fat* 23g
- *Saturates* 2.5g
- *GI* Low

serves 4

Spanish Chicken with Preserved Lemons

Ingredients

- 1 tbsp plain flour
- 4 chicken quarters, skin on
- 2 tbsp olive oil
- 2 garlic cloves, crushed
- 1 large Spanish onion, thinly sliced
- 750 ml/1 1/4 pints low-salt chicken stock
- 1/2 tsp saffron strands
- 2 yellow peppers, deseeded and cut into chunks
- 2 preserved lemons, cut into quarters
- 250 g/9 oz brown basmati rice
- white pepper
- 12 pimento-stuffed green olives
- chopped fresh parsley, to garnish
- green salad, to serve

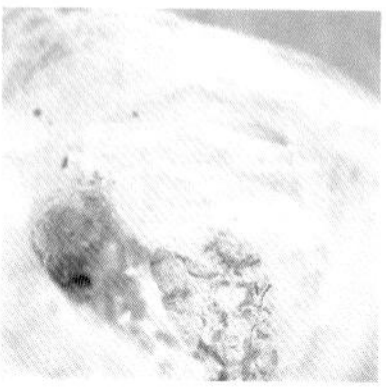

1 Preheat the oven to 180°C/350°F/Gas Mark 4. Put the flour into a large freezer bag. Add the chicken, close the top of the bag and shake to coat with flour.

2 Heat the oil in a large frying pan over a low heat, add the garlic and cook for 1 minute, stirring constantly.

3 Add the chicken to the pan and cook over a medium heat, turning frequently, for 5 minutes, or until the skin has lightly browned, then remove to a plate. Add the onion to the pan and cook, stirring occasionally, for 10 minutes until soft.

4 Meanwhile, put the stock and saffron into a saucepan over a low heat and heat through.

5 Transfer the chicken and onion to a large casserole dish, add the yellow peppers, lemons and rice, then pour over the stock. Mix well and season to taste with pepper.

6 Cover and cook in the preheated oven for 50 minutes, or until the chicken is cooked through and tender. Reduce the oven temperature to 160°C/325°F/Gas Mark 3. Add the olives to the casserole and cook for a further 10 minutes.

7 Serve scattered with parsley and accompanied by a green salad.

Nutritional Fact

Although the lemons here are high in sugar, the chicken and basmati rice slow down sugar release into the bloodstream.

Serving Analysis

- *Calories* 547
- *Protein* 26g
- *Carbohydrate* 63g
- *Sugars* 5.7g
- *Fat* 22g
- *Saturates* 3.1g
- *GI* Medium

Vegetarian

 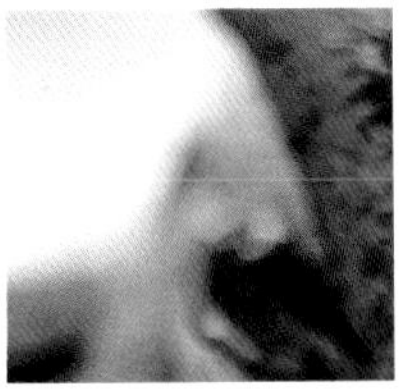 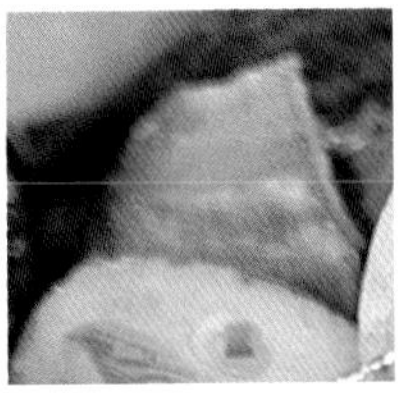 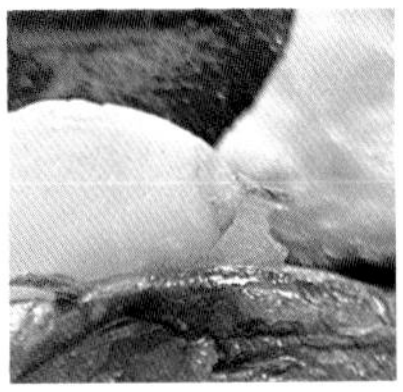 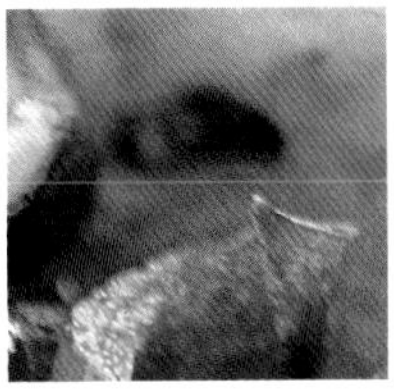 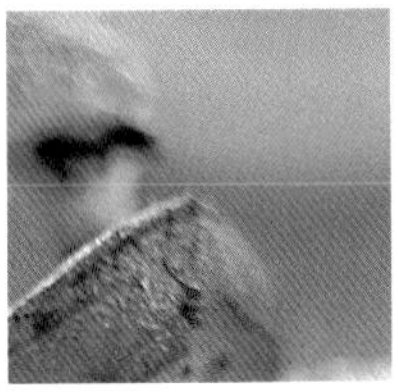

A revolution in vegetarian cooking means it is no longer considered the poor relation to cooking with meat or fish. Sophisticated ingredients drawn from a wide range of cuisines have made it now more popular than ever. A diet that contains plenty of vegetables will provide more fibre and more antioxidants and will usually be lower in fat. None of this means dull eating – as demonstrated by the recipes in this chapter.

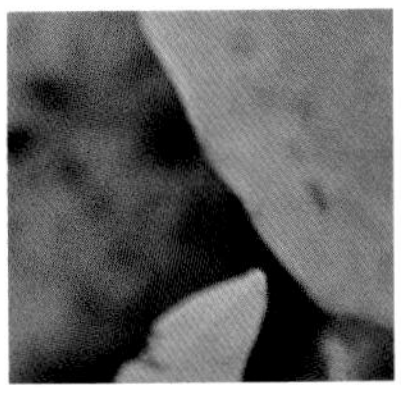 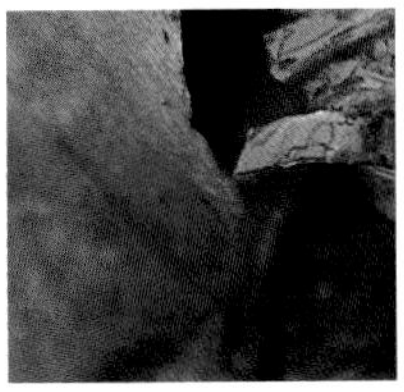 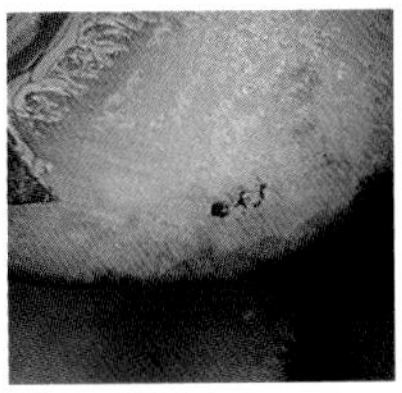 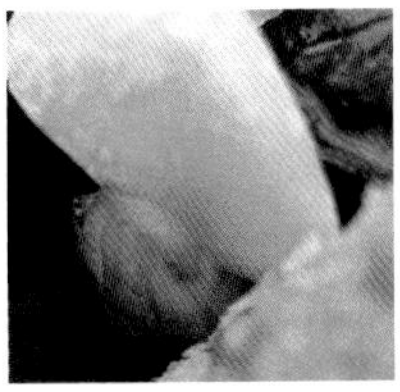 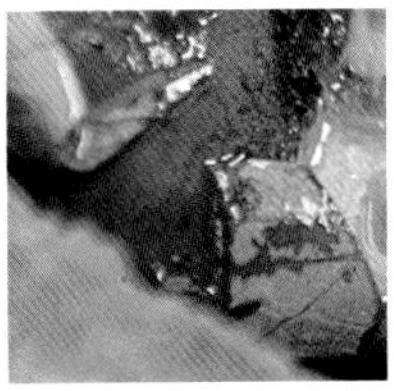 

serves 4

Celeriac, Chestnut, Spinach & Feta Filo Pies

Ingredients

- 4 tbsp olive oil
- 2 garlic cloves, crushed
- 1/2 large or 1 whole small head celeriac, cut into matchsticks
- 250 g/9 oz baby spinach leaves
- 85 g/3 oz cooked, peeled chestnuts, roughly chopped
- 200 g/7 oz feta cheese (drained weight), crumbled
- 1 egg
- 2 tbsp pesto sauce
- 1 tbsp finely chopped fresh parsley
- pepper
- 4 sheets filo pastry, about 32 cm x 18 cm/13 in x 7 in each
- green salad, to serve

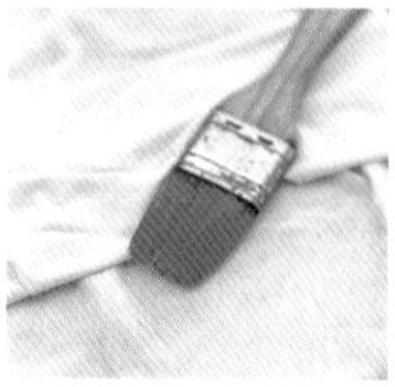

1 Preheat the oven to 190°C/375°F/Gas Mark 5. Heat 1 tablespoon of the oil in a large frying pan over a medium heat, add the garlic and cook for 1 minute, stirring constantly. Add the celeriac and cook until for 5 minutes, or until soft and browned. Remove from the pan and keep warm.

2 Add 1 tablespoon of the remaining oil to the pan, then add the spinach, cover and cook for 2–3 minutes, or until the spinach has wilted. Uncover and cook until any liquid has evaporated.

3 Mix the garlic and celeriac, spinach, chestnuts, cheese, egg, pesto, parsley and pepper to taste in a large bowl. Divide the mixture between 4 individual gratin dishes or put it all into 1 medium gratin dish.

4 Brush each sheet of filo with the remaining oil and arrange on top of the celeriac mixture. Bake in the preheated oven for 15–20 minutes, or until browned. Serve immediately with a green salad.

Nutritional Fact

Spinach contains lutein. This helps to prevent the eye degeneration that is associated with diabetes.

Serving Analysis

- *Calories* 545
- *Protein* 16g
- *Carbohydrate* 32g
- *Sugars* 5.7g
- *Fat* 40g
- *Saturates* 8.7g
- *GI* Medium

serves 4

Roasted Garlic Sweet Potato, Grilled Aubergine & Pepper Salad with Mozzarella

Ingredients

- 2 sweet potatoes, peeled and cut into chunks
- 2 tbsp olive oil
- pepper
- 2 garlic cloves, crushed
- 1 large aubergine, sliced
- 2 red peppers, deseeded and sliced
- 200 g/7 oz mixed salad leaves
- 2 x 150 g/5½ oz mozzarella cheeses, drained and sliced
- wholemeal bread, to serve

For the dressing

- 1 tbsp balsamic vinegar
- 1 garlic clove, crushed
- 3 tbsp olive oil
- 1 small shallot, finely chopped
- 2 tbsp chopped mixed fresh herbs, such as tarragon, chervil and basil
- pepper

Nutritional Fact

Sweet potatoes contain beta-carotene which helps to protect the eyes, kidneys and liver from damage.

Serving Analysis

- *Calories* 524
- *Protein* 22g
- *Carbohydrate* 34g
- *Sugars* 14.3g
- *Fat* 34g
- *Saturates* 0.1g
- *GI* Medium

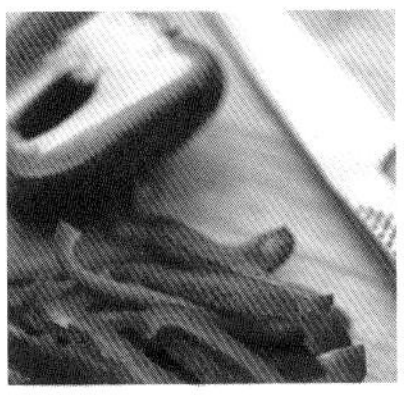

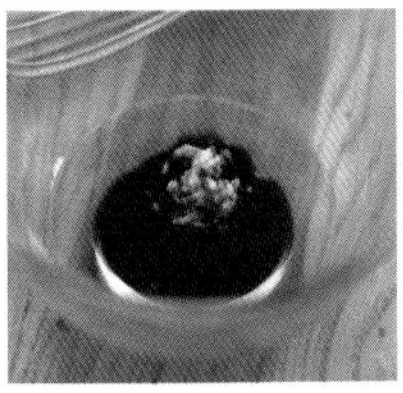

1 Preheat the oven to 190°C/375°F/Gas Mark 5. Put the sweet potato chunks into a roasting tin with the oil, pepper to taste and garlic and toss to combine. Roast in the preheated oven for 30 minutes, or until soft and slightly charred.

2 Meanwhile, preheat the grill to high. Arrange the aubergine and pepper slices on the grill pan and cook under the preheated grill, turning occasionally, for 10 minutes, or until soft and slightly charred.

3 To make the dressing, whisk the vinegar, garlic and oil together in a small bowl and stir in the shallot and herbs. Season to taste with pepper.

4 To serve, divide the salad leaves between 4 serving plates and arrange the sweet potato, aubergine, peppers and mozzarella on top. Drizzle with the dressing and serve with wholemeal bread.

serves 4

Courgette Fritters with Yogurt Dip

Ingredients

- 2–3 courgettes, about 400 g/14 oz
- 1 garlic clove, crushed
- 3 spring onions, finely sliced
- 125 g/4½ oz feta cheese (drained weight), crumbled
- 2 tbsp finely chopped fresh parsley
- 2 tbsp finely chopped fresh mint
- 1 tbsp finely chopped fresh dill
- ½ tsp freshly grated nutmeg
- 2 tbsp plain flour
- pepper
- 2 eggs
- 2 tbsp olive oil
- 1 lemon, cut into quarters, to garnish

For the dip

- 250 g/9 oz Greek yogurt
- ¼ cucumber, diced
- 1 tbsp finely chopped fresh dill
- pepper

Nutritional Fact

Eggs are one of the few vegetarian sources of protein that contain all the essential amino acids, which are the building blocks of protein.

Serving Analysis

- *Calories* 266
- *Protein* 13.3g
- *Carbohydrate* 12.6g
- *Sugars* 7g
- *Fat* 18.5g
- *Saturates* 6g
- *GI* Medium

1 Grate the courgettes straight on to a clean tea towel and cover with another. Pat well and leave for 10 minutes until the courgettes are dry.

2 Meanwhile, to make the dip, mix the yogurt, cucumber, dill and pepper to taste in a serving bowl. Cover and refrigerate.

3 Tip the courgettes into a large bowl. Stir in the garlic, spring onions, cheese, herbs, nutmeg, flour and pepper to taste. Beat the eggs in a separate bowl and stir into the courgette mixture – the mixture will be quite lumpy and uneven but this is fine.

4 Heat the oil in a large, wide saucepan over a medium heat. Drop 4 tablespoonfuls of the mixture into the pan, with space in between, and cook for 2–3 minutes on each side. Remove, drain on kitchen paper and keep warm. Cook the second batch of fritters in the same way. (There should be 8 fritters in total.)

5 Serve the fritters hot with the dip, garnished with lemon quarters.

serves 4

Mixed Mushroom Salad

Ingredients

- 3 tbsp pine kernels
- 2 red onions, cut into chunks
- 4 tbsp olive oil
- 2 garlic cloves, crushed
- 3 slices granary bread, cubed
- 200 g/7 oz mixed salad leaves
- 250 g/9 oz chestnut mushrooms, sliced
- 150 g/5½ oz shiitake mushrooms, sliced
- 150 g/5½ oz oyster mushrooms, torn

For the dressing

- 1 garlic clove, crushed
- 2 tbsp red wine vinegar
- 4 tbsp walnut oil
- 1 tbsp finely chopped fresh parsley
- pepper

1 Preheat the oven to 180°C/350°F/Gas Mark 4. Heat a non-stick frying pan over a medium heat, add the pine kernels and cook, turning, until just browned. Tip into a bowl and set aside.

2 Put the onions and 1 tablespoon of the olive oil into a roasting tin and toss to coat. Roast in the preheated oven for 30 minutes.

3 Meanwhile, heat 1 tablespoon of the remaining oil with the garlic in the non-stick frying pan over a high heat. Add the bread and cook, turning frequently, for 5 minutes, or until brown and crisp. Remove from the pan and set aside.

4 Divide the salad leaves between 4 serving plates and add the roasted onions. To make the dressing, whisk the garlic, vinegar and oil together in a small bowl. Stir in the parsley and season to taste with pepper. Drizzle over the salad and onions.

5 Heat the remaining oil in a frying pan, add the chestnut and shiitake mushrooms and cook for 2–3 minutes, stirring frequently. Add the oyster mushrooms and cook for a further 2–3 minutes. Divide the hot mushroom mixture between the 4 plates. Scatter over the pine kernels and croûtons and serve.

Nutritional Fact

Pine kernels are a source of omega-6 oils that help control blood-sugar levels and regulate cholesterol.

Serving Analysis

- *Calories* 409
- *Protein* 8g
- *Carbohydrate* 27g
- *Sugars* 6.1g
- *Fat* 32.5g
- *Saturates* 2.7g
- *GI* Low

serves 4

Baked Herb Ricotta

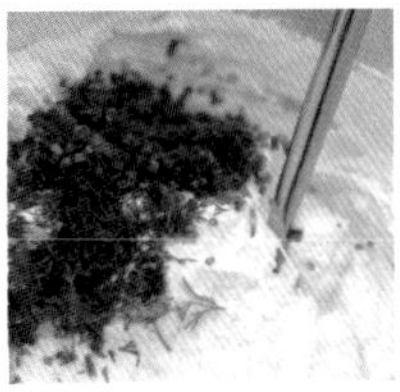

Ingredients

- 1 tbsp olive oil, plus extra for drizzling
- 1 kg/2 lb 4 oz fresh ricotta cheese, drained
- 3 eggs, lightly beaten
- 3 tbsp chopped fresh herbs, such as tarragon, parsley, dill and chives
- pepper
- 1/2 tsp paprika, plus extra for sprinkling
- 4 slices granary bread
- green salad, to serve

1 Preheat the oven to 180°C/350°F/Gas Mark 4. Brush a 1-kg/2-lb 4 oz non-stick loaf tin with the oil.

2 Put the ricotta into a bowl and beat well. Add the eggs and stir until smooth, then stir in the herbs, pepper to taste and paprika.

3 Spoon the mixture into the prepared tin and put into a roasting tin half-filled with water. Bake in the preheated oven for 30–40 minutes, or until set. Remove from the oven and leave to cool.

4 Meanwhile, cut the crusts off the bread to make Melba toast. Cut each slice widthways in half to create 2 thin slices. Cut each half diagonally into triangles. Arrange in a single layer on a baking sheet and bake in the oven for 10 minutes.

5 Turn the baked ricotta out on to a serving dish, drizzle with a little oil and sprinkle with paprika. Serve with the Melba toast and a green salad.

Nutritional Fact

This dish is very low in GI values, and so helps to stabilize blood-sugar levels, as well as providing good levels of protein.

Serving Analysis

• Calories	399
• Protein	29g
• Carbohydrate	13g
• Sugars	1.5g
• Fat	26g
• Saturates	1.4g
• GI	Low

serves 4

Chilli Bean Cakes with Avocado Salsa

Ingredients

55 g/2 oz pine kernels

425 g/15 oz canned mixed beans, drained and rinsed

1/2 red onion, finely chopped

1 tbsp tomato purée

1/2 fresh red chilli, deseeded and finely chopped

55 g/2 oz fresh brown breadcrumbs

1 egg, beaten

1 tbsp finely chopped fresh coriander

2 tbsp sunflower oil

1 lime, cut into quarters, to garnish

4 toasted granary bread rolls, to serve (optional)

For the salsa

1 avocado, stoned, peeled and chopped

100 g/3 1/2 oz tomatoes, deseeded and chopped

2 garlic cloves, crushed

2 tbsp finely chopped fresh coriander

1 tbsp olive oil

pepper

juice of 1/2 lime

1 Heat a non-stick frying pan over a medium heat, add the pine kernels and cook, turning, until just browned. Tip into a bowl and set aside.

2 Put the beans into a large bowl and roughly mash. Add the onion, tomato purée, chilli, pine kernels and half the breadcrumbs and mix well. Add half the egg and the coriander and mash together, adding a little more egg, if needed, to bind the mixture.

3 Form the mixture into 4 flat cakes. Coat with the remaining breadcrumbs, cover and chill in the refrigerator for 30 minutes.

4 To make the salsa, mix all the ingredients together in a serving bowl, cover and refrigerate until required.

5 Heat the oil in a frying pan over a medium heat, add the bean cakes and cook for 4–5 minutes on each side, or until crisp and heated through. Remove from the pan and drain on kitchen paper.

6 Serve each bean cake in a toasted granary roll, if desired, with the salsa, garnished with a lime quarter.

Nutritional Fact

Avocados are high in beneficial fats; garlic and beans help control blood-sugar levels.

Serving Analysis

- *Calories* 404
- *Protein* 13.4g
- *Carbohydrate* 31g
- *Sugars* 4.8g
- *Fat* 27.5g
- *Saturates* 3.8g
- *GI* Low

serves 4

Warm Red Lentil Salad with Goat's Cheese

Ingredients

- 2 tbsp olive oil
- 2 tsp cumin seeds
- 2 garlic cloves, crushed
- 2 tsp grated fresh root ginger
- 300 g/10½ oz split red lentils
- 700 ml/1¼ pints vegetable stock
- 2 tbsp chopped fresh mint
- 2 tbsp chopped fresh coriander
- 2 red onions, thinly sliced
- 200 g/7 oz baby spinach leaves
- 1 tsp hazelnut oil
- 150 g/5½ oz soft goat's cheese
- 4 tbsp Greek yogurt
- pepper
- 1 lemon, cut into quarters, to garnish
- toasted rye bread, to serve

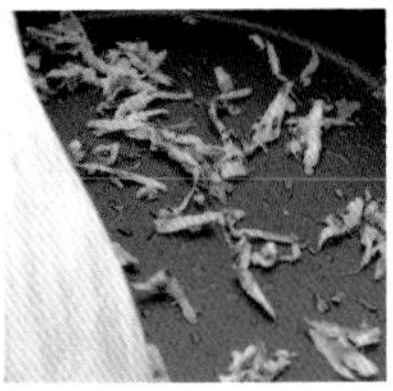

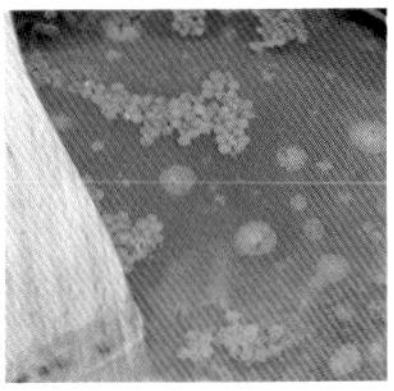

Nutritional Fact

Lentils and spinach contain B vitamins and iron. These are important for energy production and controlling sugar cravings.

Serving Analysis

• *Calories*	*310*
• *Protein*	*16g*
• *Carbohydrate*	*24g*
• *Sugars*	*6g*
• *Fat*	*17g*
• *Saturates*	*5.9g*
• *GI*	*Low*

1 Heat half the olive oil in a large saucepan over a medium heat, add the cumin seeds, garlic and ginger and cook for 2 minutes, stirring constantly.

2 Stir in the lentils, then add the stock, a ladleful at a time, until it is all absorbed, stirring constantly – this will take about 20 minutes. Remove from the heat and stir in the herbs.

3 Meanwhile, heat the remaining olive oil in a frying pan over a medium heat, add the onions and cook, stirring frequently, for 10 minutes, or until soft and lightly browned.

4 Toss the spinach in the hazelnut oil in a bowl, then divide between 4 serving plates.

5 Mash the goat's cheese with the yogurt in a small bowl and season to taste with pepper.

6 Divide the lentils between the serving plates and top with the onions and goat's cheese mixture. Garnish with lemon quarters and serve with toasted rye bread.

serves 4

Vegetable Brochettes with Jerusalem Artichoke Hummus

Ingredients

- 8 shallots, peeled
- 8 button mushrooms
- 2 yellow courgettes, cut into rounds
- 2 red peppers, deseeded and cut into chunks
- 1 small aubergine, cut into chunks
- 1 sweet potato, peeled and cut into chunks
- 2 tbsp olive oil
- juice of 1 lemon
- 1 fresh rosemary sprig, leaves removed and finely chopped
- toasted granary bread, rubbed with a halved garlic clove, to serve

For the hummus

- 350 g/12 oz Jerusalem artichokes
- 1 tbsp olive oil
- 1 tbsp butter
- 175 ml/6 fl oz milk
- 300 g/10½ oz cooked chickpeas, or canned ones, drained and rinsed
- 1 tsp ground cumin
- 2 tbsp lemon juice
- 1 garlic clove, crushed
- pepper

1 Presoak 8 wooden skewers in cold water for 30 minutes, then drain. Thread an equal quantity of the vegetables on to the skewers and put into a shallow, non-metallic dish. Mix the oil, lemon juice and rosemary together in a small bowl and pour over the skewers. Cover and leave to marinate at room temperature for 30 minutes.

2 Meanwhile, to make the hummus, put the artichokes into a large saucepan of boiling water and cook for 5 minutes, or until tender. Drain, transfer the artichokes to a food processor or blender with the oil, butter and milk and process until smooth. Add the chickpeas, cumin, lemon juice, garlic and pepper to taste and process again until smooth. Transfer to a serving dish.

3 Preheat the grill to medium. Lift the brochettes from the marinade, arrange on the grill pan and cook under the preheated grill for 15 minutes, turning frequently, until the vegetables are soft and flecked with brown.

4 Serve the brochettes immediately with the hummus and toasted granary bread rubbed with garlic.

Nutritional Fact

Jerusalem artichokes contain inulin, a natural fructose that can help to lower insulin levels.

Serving Analysis

- *Calories* 413
- *Protein* 11g
- *Carbohydrate* 60g
- *Sugars* 17.4g
- *Fat* 16.6g
- *Saturates* 3g
- *GI* Medium

Desserts & Baking

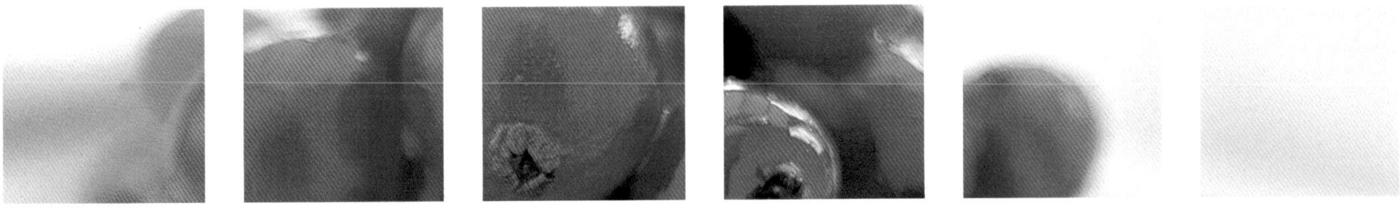

A wide range of sweets and puddings can be eaten by people with diabetes, as long as the right ingredients are used. Fruit desserts are particularly good, while fools, sorbets and frozen desserts made with low-fat yogurt are also suitable. Vary the combinations and make use of the wide selection of exotic fruits now available to enjoy delicious healthy desserts.

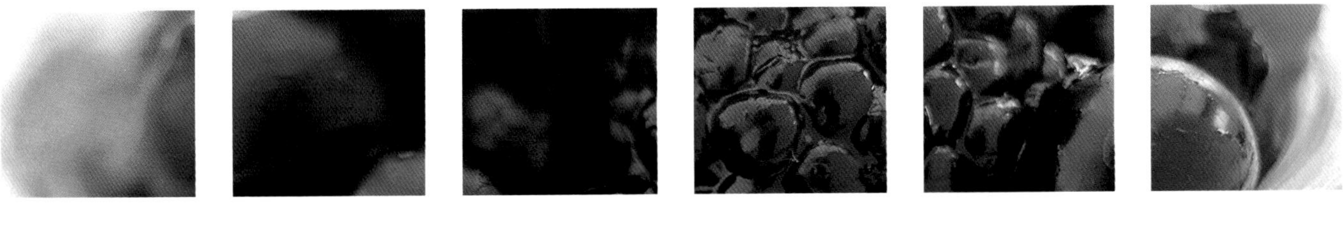

serves 4

Blueberry Frozen Yogurt

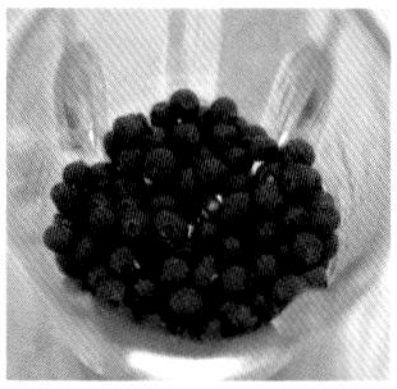

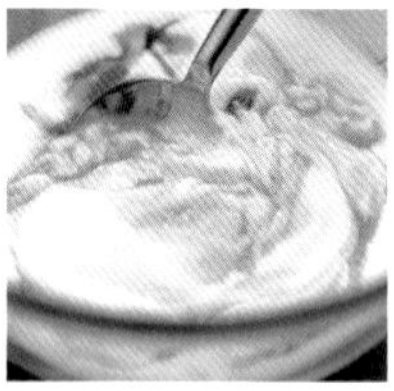

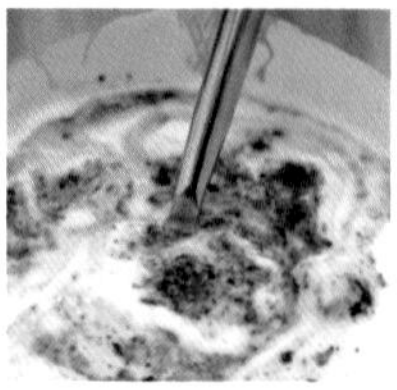

Ingredients

175 g/6 oz fresh blueberries

finely grated rind and juice of 1 orange

3 tbsp maple syrup

500 g/1 lb 2 oz natural low-fat yogurt

Nutritional Fact

Blueberries may increase sensitivity to insulin and help to control Type II diabetes.

Serving Analysis

• *Calories*	*157*
• *Protein*	*7g*
• *Carbohydrate*	*29g*
• *Sugars*	*26g*
• *Fat*	*2g*
• *Saturates*	*1.1g*
• *GI*	*Low*

1 Put the blueberries and orange juice into a food processor or blender and process to a purée. Strain through a nylon sieve into a bowl or jug.

2 Stir the maple syrup and yogurt together in a large mixing bowl, then fold in the fruit purée.

3 Churn the mixture in an ice-cream machine, following the manufacturer's instructions, then freeze for 5–6 hours. If you don't have an ice-cream machine, transfer the mixture to a freezerproof container and freeze for 2 hours. Remove from the freezer, turn out into a bowl and beat until smooth. Return to the freezer and freeze until firm.

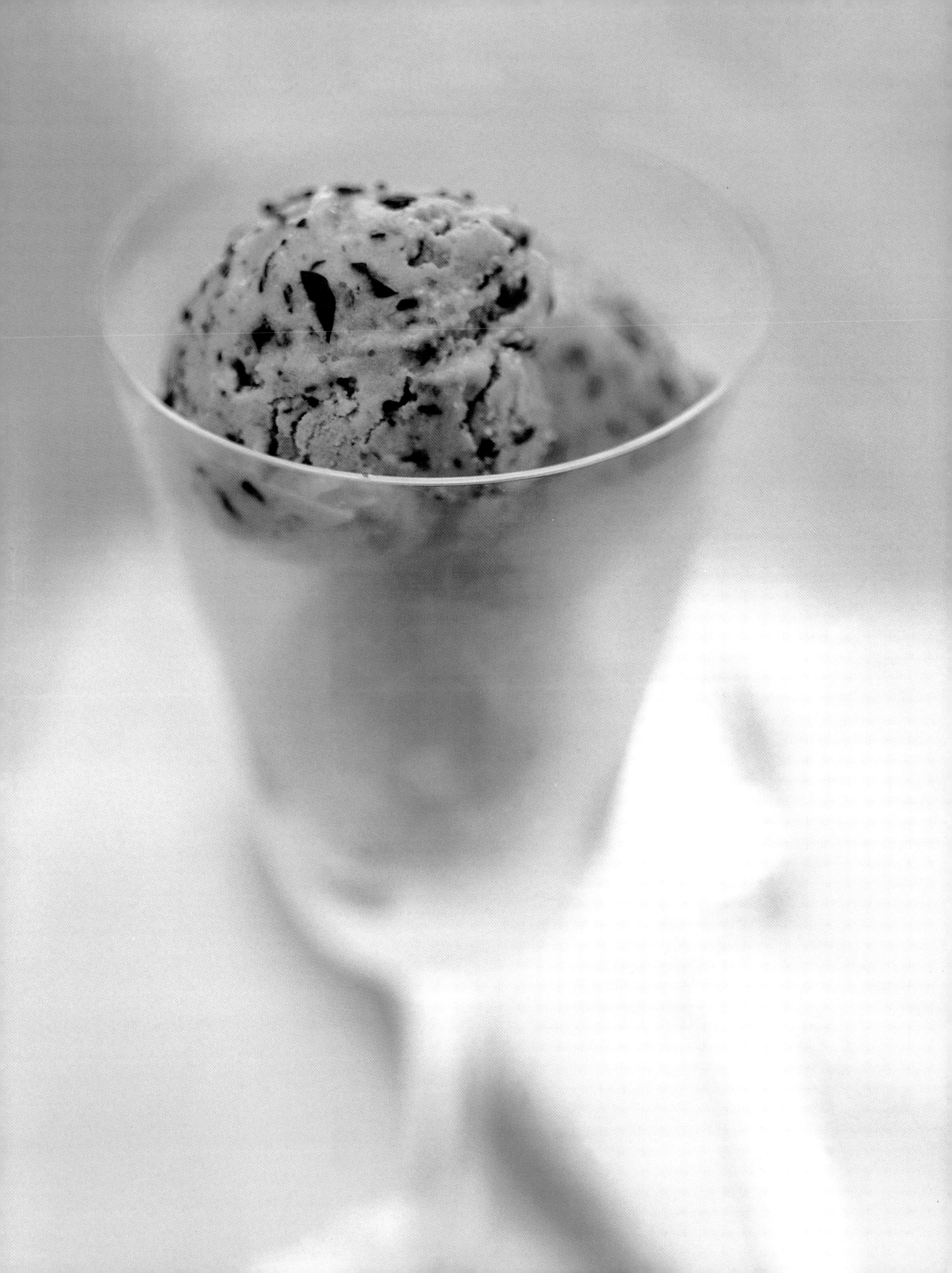

serves 4

Peach & Ginger Fool

Ingredients

- 400 g/14 oz ripe peaches
- 1 tsp chopped stem ginger in syrup
- 500 g/1 lb 2 oz natural low-fat yogurt
- 3 tbsp ginger syrup from the stem ginger
- 4 amaretti biscuits, crushed

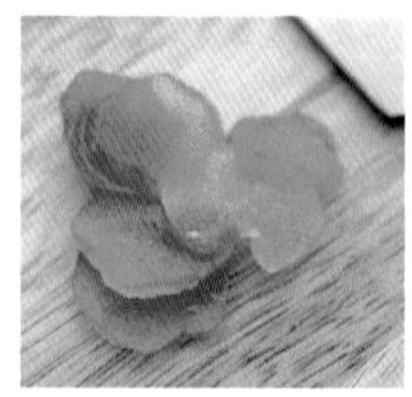

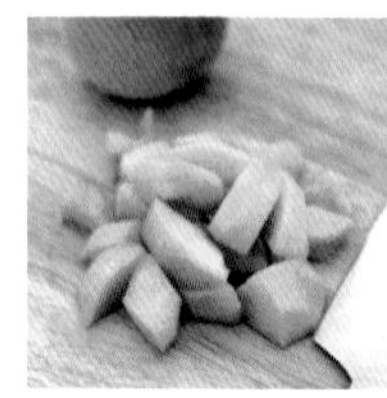

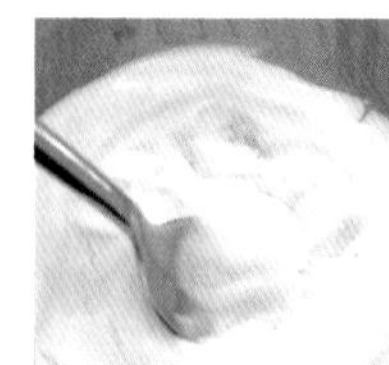

Nutritional Fact

Peaches have a low GI score, and ginger lowers cholesterol and improves circulation.

Serving Analysis

- *Calories* *300*
- *Protein* *11g*
- *Carbohydrate* *37g*
- *Sugars* *32.5g*
- *Fat* *6.7g*
- *Saturates* *1.5g*
- *GI* *Medium*

1 Put the peaches into a large, heatproof bowl and cover with boiling water. Leave for 1 minute. Using a slotted spoon, lift out the fruit. When cool enough to handle, peel away the skins, remove and discard the stones and roughly chop the flesh. Transfer to a food processor or blender, add the ginger and process to a purée.

2 Stir the yogurt and ginger syrup together in a bowl.

3 Spoon a little of the yogurt mixture into 4 serving glasses, then top with a spoonful of the fruit purée. Repeat until the mixtures are used up. Chill in the refrigerator for 3 hours.

4 Scatter over the crushed amaretti biscuits before serving.

serves 4

Summer Fruit Elderflower Jelly

Ingredients

- 4 leaves gelatine
- 75 ml/2 1/2 fl oz boiling water
- 30 ml/1 fl oz elderflower cordial
- 175 ml/6 fl oz cold water
- 200 g/7 oz mixed berries, such as raspberries, redcurrants and blackberries
- 4 tsp single cream

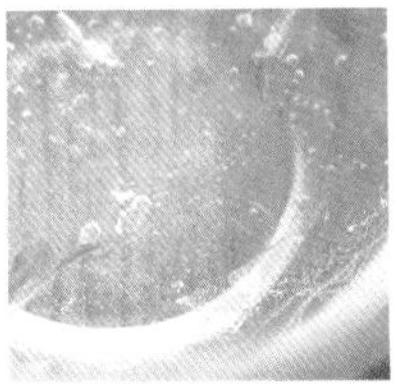

Nutritional Fact

Berries in general provide certain plant chemicals. These give them their colours and help to balance blood sugar.

Serving Analysis

• *Calories*	*67*
• *Protein*	*6.7g*
• *Carbohydrate*	*9.6g*
• *Sugars*	*4.9g*
• *Fat*	*0.5g*
• *Saturates*	*0.2g*
• *GI*	*Low*

1 Soak the gelatine leaves in a bowl of cold water for 10 minutes. Lift out and squeeze gently, then mix with the boiling water in a heatproof bowl. Stir until the gelatine has completely dissolved.

2 Stir in the elderflower cordial and cold water.

3 Divide the berries between 4 wine glasses and pour over the elderflower mixture. Chill in the refrigerator for 3 hours.

4 Serve each jelly with a spoonful of cream.

serves 4

Grilled Honeyed Figs with Sabayon

Ingredients

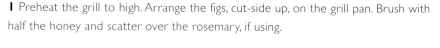

8 fresh figs, cut in half
4 tbsp clear honey
2 fresh rosemary sprigs, leaves removed and finely chopped (optional)
3 eggs

1 Preheat the grill to high. Arrange the figs, cut-side up, on the grill pan. Brush with half the honey and scatter over the rosemary, if using.

2 Cook under the preheated grill for 5–6 minutes, or until just beginning to caramelize.

3 Meanwhile, to make the sabayon, in a large, heatproof bowl, lightly whisk the eggs with the remaining honey, then place over a saucepan of simmering water. Using a hand-held electric whisk, beat the eggs and honey together for 10 minutes, or until pale and thick.

4 Put 4 fig halves on each of 4 serving plates, add a generous spoonful of the sabayon and serve immediately.

Nutritional Fact

Fresh figs release their sugars much more slowly than dried ones. They contain minerals that can help with insulin sensitivity.

Serving Analysis

- *Calories* *190*
- *Protein* *5.4g*
- *Carbohydrate* *36g*
- *Sugars* *32g*
- *Fat* *4g*
- *Saturates* *1.2g*
- *GI* *Medium*

serves 4

Little Dark Chocolate Mousse Pots with Poached Berries

Nutritional Fact

Dark chocolate is lower in sugar than milk chocolate and can be an occasional treat if eaten in small amounts, such as in this recipe.

Serving Analysis

- *Calories* 241
- *Protein* 4.4g
- *Carbohydrate* 24g
- *Sugars* 20g
- *Fat* 16g
- *Saturates* 8.7g
- *GI* Medium

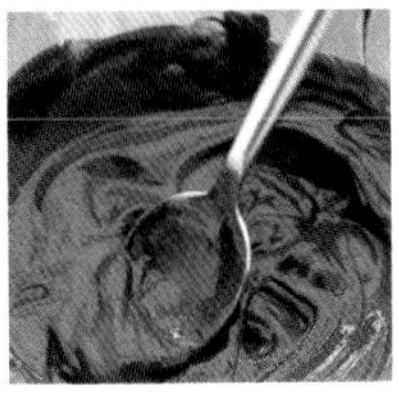

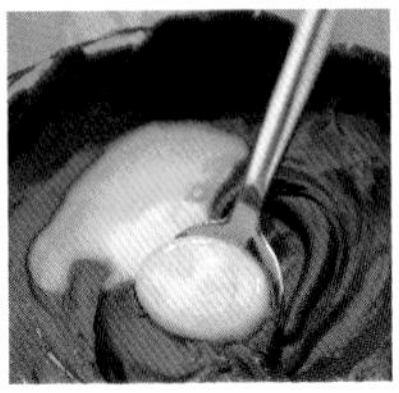

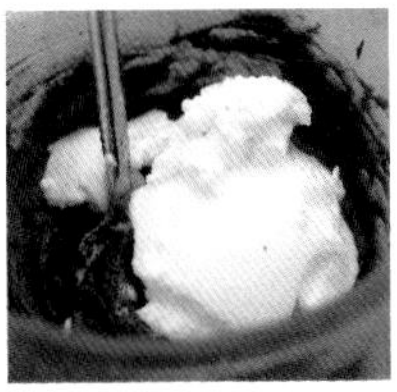

Ingredients

- 100 g/3½ oz plain dark chocolate, minimum 70% cocoa solids
- 25 g/1 oz unsalted butter
- 2 eggs, separated
- 1 tbsp maple syrup
- 100 g/3½ oz mixed dark berries, such as blackberries, blackcurrants and blueberries
- 1 tbsp crème de cassis
- fresh mint leaves, to decorate

1 Break the chocolate into pieces, put into a heatproof bowl with the butter and place over a saucepan of simmering water. Leave to melt, then allow to cool slightly. Stir in the egg yolks and maple syrup.

2 Whisk the egg whites in a large bowl until stiff, then fold into the cooled chocolate mixture. Divide between 4 ramekins and chill in the refrigerator for 3 hours.

3 Meanwhile, put the berries into a small saucepan with the crème de cassis over a low heat and cook for 5–10 minutes, or until the berries are glossy and soft. Leave to cool.

4 To serve, spoon the berries on top of the chocolate mousse and decorate with mint leaves.

makes 16

Nutty Muesli Squares

Ingredients

- 115 g/4 oz unsalted butter, plus extra for greasing
- 4 tbsp clear honey
- 25 g/1 oz unrefined caster sugar
- 250 g/9 oz porridge oats
- 25 g/1 oz dried cranberries
- 25 g/1 oz stoned dates, chopped
- 25 g/1 oz hazelnuts, chopped
- 70 g/2½ oz flaked almonds

1 Preheat the oven to 190°C/375°F/Gas Mark 5. Grease a 20-cm/8-inch square baking tin.

2 Melt the butter with the honey and sugar in a saucepan and stir together. Add the remaining ingredients and mix thoroughly.

3 Turn the mixture into the prepared tin and press down well. Bake in the preheated oven for 20–30 minutes.

4 Remove from the oven and leave to cool in the tin. Cut into 16 squares.

Nutritional Fact

Oats and nuts ensure the slow release of sugars and are, therefore, good sources of energy, which can help to alleviate sugar cravings.

Serving Analysis

- *Calories* 167
- *Protein* 3.3g
- *Carbohydrate* 17g
- *Sugars* 6.9g
- *Fat* 10g
- *Saturates* 4g
- *GI* Medium

serves 4

Walnut & Pecan Soda Bread

Nutritional Fact
Walnuts are a very good source of omega-3 and -6 oils, which help to balance blood sugar.

Serving Analysis

• *Calories*	*613*
• *Protein*	*17g*
• *Carbohydrate*	*94g*
• *Sugars*	*7.2g*
• *Fat*	*19g*
• *Saturates*	*2.1g*
• *GI*	*Medium*

Ingredients

- 450 g/1 lb plain flour, plus extra for flouring
- 1 tsp bicarbonate of soda
- 1 tsp cream of tartar
- 1 tsp salt
- 1 tsp sugar
- 50 g/1 3/4 oz chopped walnuts
- 50 g/1 3/4 oz chopped pecans nuts
- 300 ml/10 fl oz buttermilk

1 Preheat the oven to 180°/350°F/Gas Mark 4. Dust a baking sheet with flour.

2 Sift the flour, bicarbonate of soda, cream of tartar and salt into a large mixing bowl. Stir in the sugar and nuts. Pour in the buttermilk and mix to a soft dough.

3 With floured hands, knead the dough briefly on a lightly floured work surface, then shape into a round 20–25 cm/8–10 inches in diameter and transfer to the prepared baking sheet. Cut a cross in the top of the dough.

4 Bake in the preheated oven for 30 minutes, then cover with foil and bake for a further 15 minutes.

5 Remove from the oven and allow to cool slightly. Serve warm in slices.

serves 4

Melon & Ginger Sorbet

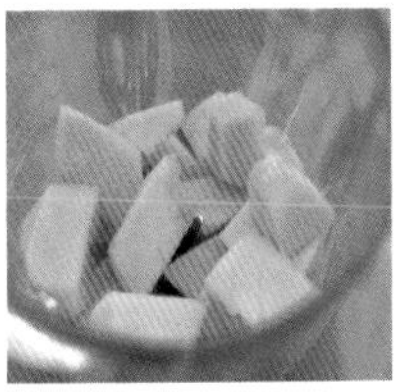

Ingredients

- 1 ripe melon, peeled, deseeded and cut into chunks
- juice of 2 limes
- 1 tbsp grated fresh root ginger
- 4 tbsp unrefined caster sugar
- 1 egg white, lightly whisked
- fresh strawberries or raspberries, to serve

1 Put the melon, lime juice and ginger into a food processor or blender and process until smooth. Pour into a measuring jug and make up to 600 ml/ 1 pint with cold water.

2 Pour into a bowl and stir in the sugar. Beat in the egg white.

3 Transfer to a freezerproof container and freeze for 6 hours.

4 Serve in scoops with strawberries or raspberries.

Nutritional Fact

Melon contains good levels of vitamin C. This vitamin is necessary for blood-sugar control. It can also help to strengthen arteries.

Serving Analysis

- *Calories* 141
- *Protein* 2.56g
- *Carbohydrate* 36g
- *Sugars* 33g
- *Fat* 0.4g
- *Saturates* 0.1g
- *GI* Medium

Index